Recipes for *Living*

Virginia M. Pribyl, L.D.

First Edition, October 1988
Second Printing, June 1989
Second Edition, July 1990

Published by VMP Services, P.O. Box 713, Arlington, TX 76004

Library of Congress Catalog Card Number: 88-90266

International Standard Book Number: 0-9621089-0-1

A 🐾 Publication   Printed by Wimmer Brothers, Inc. - Memphis - Dallas

Contents

Recipes

Acknowledgments

I especially want to thank:

Neva Cochran, M.S.,R.D./L.D., President-elect of The Texas Dietetic Association, and Joseph C. Magliolo, M.D., for reviewing the book for technical accuracy.

Lynda Blakeslee, Licensed Professional Counselor, for writing the section on Nutrition and Stress and for her helpful suggestions during the entire project.

John Pribyl, my husband, for serving as editor, artist and book designer. Without his help and support, the book would not yet be completed.

Pat, Steve and Bill, our sons, for proofing manuscript and providing ideas to make the text more readable.

Anne Marie, our daughter, who took on extra household duties while I was working on the book.

All my family and friends for their good nature as I've tested recipes over the years. You made the book possible.

Introduction

If you are like many of the people I teach, you're interested in eating right. You may know what you should eat, but need help applying that knowledge to everyday living. Or you may already be eating well but are looking for new recipe ideas that will contribute to an even healthier way of eating. Either way, *Recipes for Living* is for you.

This book is a collection of practical knowlege and healthy eating practices that I have developed over my years of experience as a dietitian, and particularly over the past five years of teaching. I hope to give you a practical, everyday approach for improving the way you eat without having to give up your favorite foods.

Many of the recipes in this book are modifications of traditional family recipes. A number of them are quick to prepare and do not require a lot of skill. The recipes are designed to minimize fat, cholesterol, sodium, and sugar while providing healthy amounts of complex carbohydrates and fiber. Many are low calorie versions of the original recipes, sometimes with spices, herbs, or wine added to improve the flavor.

When you eat to promote good health and longer life, calories, fat, cholesterol and sodium are significant items which need to be watched closely. A computer-generated breakdown is given with each recipe in this book that shows the amount of calories, fat, cholesterol and sodium per serving.

People in my classes tell me that they are most interested in main dishes and vegetables, so I have included a large selection of these recipes. They also ask for dishes that may be cooked in a microwave oven. I've included microwave cooking instructions where this is a better or more practical way of cooking.

My goal in writing this cookbook is to help interested people start and continue on the road to cooking and eating healthier foods.

Food can be healthy and still taste good!

Virginia Magliolo Pribyl

Why Change the Way We Eat?

More and more of us, young and old, realize the food we eat can have a great impact on our health and well-being. We're always looking for ways to improve our eating habits because we want to live a long healthy life. The American Heart Association (AHA), one of the most active and respected health organizations in the nation, offers help in this regard. Their mission is to prevent or reduce the incidence of coronary heart disease, the number one cause of death in our country.

According to AHA research, the risk factors for heart attack are high blood cholesterol level, high blood pressure, cigarette smoking, diabetes, excessive weight, lack of exercise and a family history of heart disease.

While we can't change our family history, we can control many of these risk factors, including those having to do with our eating habits. The American Heart Association recommends for all persons over the age of two:

- **Reduce total fat intake.**
- **Limit cholesterol to 300 milligrams a day.**
- **Drink alcoholic beverages in moderation, if at all.**

Statistics from the National Cancer Institute indicate that about *one-third of all cancer deaths may be related to what we eat.* Their recommendations for the way healthy Americans should be eating are compatible with those of the American Heart Association:

- **Eat foods high in dietary fiber daily (fresh fruits, vegetables, and whole-grain breads and cereals).**
- **Eat foods low in dietary fat.**
- **Drink alcoholic beverages in moderation, if at all.**

The U.S. Department of Agriculture and the U.S. Department of Health and Human Services have also published guidelines for the way people in our country should eat to stay healthy:

- **Eat a variety of foods.**

- **Maintain desirable weight.**

- **Avoid too much fat, saturated fat, and cholesterol.**

- **Eat foods with adequate starch and fiber.**

- **Avoid too much sugar.**

- **Avoid too much sodium.**

- **If you drink alcoholic beverages, do so in moderation.**

As you can see, many of the best experts in our country think the same way. But did you know it is not necessary to eliminate any particular food from your diet? The emphasis is on moderation: choose the recommended foods more often and save the suspect foods for occasional use.

Reduce Fats In Your Diet for Healthier Living

Americans have no problem getting the very small amount of fat their body requires each day. Only one teaspoon (5 grams) of corn oil is sufficient to supply the daily needed amount of essential fatty acid for an adult. * When you realize that a small fast food hamburger and french fries contain over five teaspoons (25 grams) of fat, it doesn't take an expert to tell us most people consume fat in far greater amounts than their body needs. This is a major contributer to health problems including obesity, high blood cholesterol, and increased risk for some types of cancer.

Where does all this fat come from? Some foods, like butter, margarine, shortening and oil are obvious sources of

* Whitney, G.A., Hamilton. E.M. and Boyle, M.A., Understanding Nutrition, Third Edition (1984) St. Paul, MN: West

fat. Whole milk, cheese, ice cream, nuts, seeds, salad dressings, poultry skin, well-marbled meats and some bakery products also provide large amounts of fat.

If you make a habit of eating deep-fat fried or breaded foods, or fatty meats such as bacon, sausage, and luncheon meats, you are getting more fat than you need. High-fat desserts such as pies, pastries and some cakes, and rich sauces and gravies, also contribute a great deal of fat to the diet.

For healthier living and longer lifespan, it is important to decrease the amount of fat in your diet.

Three Kinds of Fats, Some Better Than Others

It's unhealthy to eat too much fat, but not all fat is bad for you. The most important thing to remember is to limit saturated fats, the ones that increase blood cholesterol levels.

According to the American Heart Association, calories from fat should be limited to thirty percent of total daily calories. Within this thirty percent, ten percent or less should come from "saturated" fats, ten percent or less from "polyunsaturated" fats, with the remainder from "monounsaturated" fats.

1. Saturated fats. A diet high in saturated fats raises the level of blood cholesterol and therefore increases the risk of heart attack.

Saturated fats come mostly from foods of animal origin and are usually solid at room temperature. Meats such as beef, veal, lamb, and pork, and dairy products such as whole milk, butter, some cheeses and cream are sources of saturated fats.

Saturated fats are also found in several foods of plant origin—coconut oil, palm oil and palm kernel oil. These oils, some of the worst things for our body, are the most highly saturated of all fats. They are everywhere: in breakfast cereals, cake mixes, nondairy coffee creamers, crackers, bakery goods, and potato chips. Many fast food restaurants cook french fries in some of these oils.

2. Polyunsaturated fats. When polyunsaturated oils are substituted for part of the saturated fats in the diet, blood levels of cholesterol decrease.

Plant oils are high in polyunsaturates, the fats that are usually liquid at room temperature. Oils such as safflower, cottonseed, corn, soybeans, and sunflower seed are high in polyunsaturated fats. Use these oils for cooking instead of solid shortening which is a saturated fat.

3. Monounsaturated fats. Until recently it was believed that monounsaturated fats had little effect on cholesterol levels. New research indicates at least one of the monounsaturated fats, olive oil, may help control cholesterol. Add a small amount of olive oil to your diet when you decrease the amount of saturated fats you eat.

Other plant sources that contain high levels of monounsaturated fats are peanut oil and rapeseed oil.

Cholesterol and a Healthy Heart

Cholesterol is a waxy, fat-like substance essential for certain body processes. All that we need is manufactured by our body. Cholesterol also comes directly from foods of animal origin, such as meat, poultry, seafood, and whole milk dairy products. Egg yolks and organ meats contain the highest concentration.

For some people, eating foods high in cholesterol tends to increase blood levels of cholesterol. However, most people don't realize that eating foods high in saturated fat tends to increase cholesterol levels even more. They mistakenly think they are guarding against heart attack by giving up eggs for breakfast.

Beware, foods labeled "no cholesterol" or "contains 100 percent vegetable shortening" may still contain a large percentage of undesirable fats. When you see a food labeled "no cholesterol," check also to see that it is low in saturated fat. For example, almost all nondairy coffee creamers contain coconut oil. Likewise, some bakery products made with "100 percent vegetable shortening" may contain palm or palm kernel oil. Coconut, palm and palm kernel oils are the most saturated of all the fats; avoid them if possible. Read the fine print; if the label says palm oil or coconut oil, leave it on the shelf. Foods of plant origin like fruits, vegetables, and grains never contain cholesterol in their natural state.

Carbohydrates, Starch, and Fiber: The Good Group

When you decrease the amount of foods containing fat and cholesterol in your diet, you should increase the number of "complex carbohydrates" that you eat. Complex carbohydrates are found in starchy foods like potatoes, corn, lima beans, pasta, rice, dry beans and peas. Also, whole grain cereal products, such as brown rice, oatmeal, and whole wheat cereals and breads are excellent sources.

Starchy foods not only provide energy, but they take longer than other carbohydrates to digest, and so tend to keep you from getting hungry too fast.

Starches, along with fruits and vegetables, provide the fiber in your diet. Dietary fiber is the material in plants that cannot be broken down in the human digestive tract. A great many people in our country need to increase the amount of fiber they eat.

11

Because there are many different types of beneficial fibers in foods, it is important to eat a variety of high fiber foods each day. Soluble fibers, found in oatmeal and oatbran, apples and other fruits, and some dry beans, may help regulate blood cholesterol levels and help lower the possibility of heart disease. Insoluble fibers, found in wheat products, help relieve constipation and may help prevent colon cancer.

Fiber comes only from plant food; there is no fiber in meat.

Simple Carbohydrates: A Temporary "Fix"

Foods like sugar, candy, jam, honey and corn syrup are simple carbohydrates. They are quickly absorbed by the body and provide only a temporary bit of energy. Unlike complex carbohydrates, they contain no fiber and few, if any, nutrients. Your body does not *require* any simple carbohydrates; complex carbohydrates can provide all the energy you need while at the same time providing essential vitamins, minerals and fiber.

A high percentage of dietary sugar comes from soft drinks, the number one beverage consumed in our country. When you drink a twelve-ounce can of regular soda you are getting mostly water with 9 to 11 teaspoons of sugar added—that's about 150 calories with no nutrients.

Weight Control to Feel Better

In almost all cases, controlling your weight is essential to maintaining good health. Weight control is a matter of balancing calorie intake from the food you eat with the calories you spend in daily activity. Many people in our country need to lose weight, but there is a small per-

12

centage of healthy people who actually need to gain weight. How does a low fat way of eating affect weight?

To Lose Weight

Although it's easier said than done, all you need to lose weight is to create a calorie deficit, that is, to use more than you take in. Reducing fat intake is a good way to start.

Calories in food come from protein, carbohydrates, and fats. Protein and carbohydrates provide four calories per gram, fats provide nine calories per gram. When you reduce fat intake you can increase the amounts of fruits, vegetables and starches you eat and still lose weight. Of all the food groups, fruits and vegetables provide the fewest calories. And contrary to what some people think, adding starchy foods is a good way to feel full after a meal while cutting calories. If you're trying to lose weight, cut down on the margarine, butter, sour cream, and gravies that usually smother starchy foods.

To Gain Weight

It is possible to gain weight while eating the low fat way: simply add as many low-fat calories as possible to what you presently eat.

According to Dr. Jean Mayer and Jeanne Goldberg, R.D., "For many people who need to gain weight, targeting their efforts at snacks seems to be most successful." *

Plan bedtime and between meal snacks, but not so close to mealtime that they affect your appetite. Choose higher calorie items such as ice milk, a small meat or peanut butter sandwich, low fat cheese and crackers, several tablespoons of peanuts or sunflower seeds,

---

* Mayer, Dr. Jean and Goldberg, Jeanne, R.D., Food for Thought, Washington Post Writers' Group (25 Feb. 1987)

dates or dried fruits like bananas, apricots or raisins, whole grain muffins and fruit breads. Remember to use polyunsaturated margarine on bread, and add a little jam or jelly. Carry a snack to work with you.

When trying to gain weight, eat higher calorie foods like meat, dry beans, potatoes, pastas, rice, and bread first. Eat bulkier foods like salads last so you don't get full before you've eaten higher calorie foods. Skip the clear soups and broths, or eat them last; they are filling and don't provide many calories.

Never skip a meal. Make it a point to relax at mealtime.

Sodium and High Blood Pressure

Some people may avoid high blood pressure by consuming less dietary sodium, most often found in salt. The American Heart Association's recommended intake of sodium is a maximum of 3000 milligrams each day. This is equivalent to a grand total of one and one-half teaspoons of salt from all sources.

The American Cancer Society recommends limiting the amount of salt-cured foods, and smoked and nitrite-cured foods. Smoked bacon, ham, hot dogs, and certain cold cuts should be eaten only occasionally.

Commercially prepared foods can contribute more than their share of dietary sodium. Foods which provide significant amounts include bakery products, cured and processed meats, canned vegetables, and many cheeses.

Foods with a nutrition label provide sodium information in milligrams. When checking foods without a nutrition label, look for words such as soda or sodium alone or as part of another word in the list of ingredients. These words on a label indicate sodium is present.

14

Alcohol

You may have heard that a small amount of alcohol can be good for your heart. The American Heart Association emphasizes that "a protective effect of alcohol has not been proven, but its many adverse effects are well documented." *

Most experts recommend you limit alcohol (this includes beer) to one or two drinks per day if you drink at all. Heavy drinking increases the risk of cancer. In addition, alcohol provides almost as many calories as fat and no significant nutrients.

It's There For the Taking

The guidelines established by experts at the American Heart Association, the National Cancer Institute, the U.S. Department of Agriculture, the U.S. Department of Health and Human Services, and elsewhere, are a valuable resource for our everyday living. If we follow the instructions from these groups we will put ourselves on the road to longer, healthier lives.

So, why change the way you eat?
...you'll feel better, and probably live longer!

---

* American Heart Association, Coronary Risk Factor Statement for the American Public (1985) Dallas, TX

15

What Should We Eat?

Our body requires a variety of foods to supply the energy and nutrients for normal growth and good health. The four food group system is a flexible, easy-to-use guide developed by the U.S. Department of Agriculture food and nutrition scientists to help us select the foods we eat. The food groups include: fruits and vegetables, bread-cereal, milk, and meat and meat alternates.

Daily Choices for a Healthy Body

For the balanced nutrition your body needs, eat the recommended daily servings from a wide variety of foods in each of the food groups. After that, eat enough additional servings (and calories) to maintain your desirable weight.

For the person interested in losing weight, following the four food group system is a way to control calories without "going on a diet." Sometimes people say, "I can't eat bread, I'm on a diet." Giving up bread, or any whole group of foods, decreases your chances of getting all the nutrients your body needs. Using the four food group system, you can have a balanced diet and still consume only 1200 calories a day, a level recommended by many weight loss diets. The breakdown looks something like this:

Fruit and Vegetables: Four Servings.
    1/2 cup of each of two
        vegetables (one starch)   105 calories
    2 fruits   160 calories
Bread-Cereal: Four servings.
    4 slices bread or 3/4 cup cereal
        substituted for one slice of bread   280 calories
Milk: Two servings.
    2 cups of 1% milk   200 calories
Meat: Two servings. (3 ounces each.)
    6 ounces of cooked meat   450 calories

            Total: 1195 calories

Note: Add 45 calories for each teaspoon of margarine, butter or salad dressing.

Food Groups

Fruit and Vegetable Group
Four Servings per Day

Fruits and vegetables are high in complex carbohydrates and fiber, low in calories, fat, and sodium, and contain no cholesterol. They provide significant amounts of vitamin C and vitamin A and are a good source of energy. Many people don't eat enough fruits and vegetables and are missing the benefits they provide.

Everyone needs a minimum of four servings from this group daily, making sure to have at least one serving of a fruit or vegetable high in vitamin C each day, and one high in vitamin A several times a week.

A serving is 1/2 cup or a typical portion such as 1/2 grapefruit, one orange or banana, a bowl of salad, or one medium potato.

Good sources of vitamin C are: oranges, grapefruit, tangerines, lemons, melons, berries, tomatoes, broccoli, potato baked in the skin.

Good sources of vitamin A are: dark-green and deep-yellow vegetables such as broccoli, greens, carrots, sweet potatoes.

Bread-Cereal or Grain Group
Four servings per day

Breads, cereals, and grains like rice or pasta provide complex carbohydrates, B vitamins, and iron. Starches and most types of dietary fiber are complex carbohydrates. An important source of energy, complex carbohydrates stay in the stomach longer than some foods, giving a feeling of fullness.

Choose whole grain and enriched low-fat breads and cereals. Whole grains provide more fiber and several additional nutrients.

Iron from foods in the bread-cereal group is more readily available to your body if you consume a food high in vitamin C at the same meal.

Calories are moderate when foods such as bread, cereal, and grains are prepared and served with little or no added butter, margarine, jelly or sugar.

Everyone needs four servings per day from this group. A serving is one slice of bread, 1/2 to 3/4 cup of cooked cereal, one ounce of dry cereal, 1/2 cup of macaroni, spaghetti, or rice, or one six-inch tortilla.

Milk Group
Two servings per day

Foods from this group are a major source of calcium in American diets, and also contain significant amounts of protein and riboflavin. Without these foods it's very difficult to get the calcium your body needs. Women, the persons most likely to develop osteoporosis, or brittle bone disease, need to insure that they have adequate servings from this group.

Choose skim or low-fat milk, low-fat buttermilk, nonfat or low-fat yogurt or low-fat cottage cheese. Look for cheeses made from skim milk, part-skim mozzarella or ricotta cheese, and other cheeses that contain no more than two grams of fat per ounce. Parmesan cheese may be used in small amounts.

Adults need two servings from the milk group daily, children two to three servings, and teenagers four servings. Children and teenagers require more servings of milk group foods because of their developing bones. Serving size is based on the amount of calcium foods contain. An eight-ounce cup of milk or yogurt counts as one serving. Calcium equal to that in a cup of milk is provided by 1 1/2 ounces of cheese, one cup of pudding, two cups of cottage cheese, or 1 3/4 cups of ice milk.

Meats, Poultry, Fish and Beans Group
Two servings per day

Foods from this group provide protein, iron, and thiamin. Most Americans get more than enough protein. Women of child-bearing age, particularly, need to insure they eat enough iron-containing foods to prevent iron deficiency anemia.

Choose dry beans such as pinto, kidney and navy beans, or dried peas such as lentils and split peas, or lean beef, veal, pork or lamb with fat trimmed away, poultry with skin removed, and fish. Peanut butter may be eaten occasionally.

19

Red meats are the best source of iron. Meats contain a form of iron easy for our body to absorb. The iron contained in dry beans and peas becomes easier to absorb if a food high in vitamin C, such as sliced tomatoes, is consumed at the same meal.

Dry beans and peas contain no cholesterol and very little fat. Combining dry beans or peas with a small amount of meat, chicken, or fish, or with dairy products or grains, makes them a better source of protein.

Fish contain less fat than meat or chicken. In addition, deep-water fish such as salmon, albacore tuna, sardines, mackerel and whitefish contain "omega-3" fatty acids which may have a beneficial effect on cholesterol. You should eat fish several times per week.

Egg yolks and organ meats, such as liver, have the highest concentrations of cholesterol; limit whole eggs or egg yolks to two or three per week. Liver may be eaten once per month.

Everyone needs only two servings per day from the meat, poultry, fish and beans group. A serving is two to three ounces of lean cooked meat, poultry, or fish without bone. (Three ounces of cooked meat is about the size of a deck of cards.) Try not to exceed a daily intake of five to seven ounces. One ounce of meat is equal to one egg, 1/2 to 3/4 cup cooked of dry beans, peas, or lentils, or two tablespoons of peanut butter.

Fats, Sweets, and Alcohol
The "Extra" Foods Group

Foods in this group include margarine, butter, mayonnaise and other salad dressings, sugar, candy, jams, jellies, syrups, soft drinks, wine, beer, liquor, and unenriched, refined bakery products.

Almost no foods from the fats, sweets, and alcohol group are required by your body. Butter and margarine provide some Vitamin A, and vegetable oils provide Vitamin E and essential fatty acids, but these are all available from other sources.

Foods from this group provide mainly calories. They may be the foods you like, but they have few redeeming virtues. Your first priority should be to select the servings of food you need from the four food groups. Then, if your calorie count will permit, add minimum amounts of foods from this group.

21

A Word About Water

Water is essential for life, being second in importance only to oxygen. You can live several weeks without food, but only a few days without water.

Water contains no nutrients, but is an essential part of all body functions. Your body, which is between forty five percent and sixty five percent water, maintains a fairly constant water content by balancing your water intake with water loss.

Beverages, meats, fruits, vegetables, cereals and breads all contain water. In addition to what you obtain in foods, it's a good idea to drink six to eight glasses of water a day.

So, what should you eat?
...lots of fruits and vegetables, whole grain breads and cereals, low-fat dairy products, fish, lean meats and chicken, and dry beans and peas.

Making Changes in the Way We Eat

When making changes to healthier eating, you don't have to give up your favorite foods. You may want to choose certain of these foods in moderate amounts or you may want to vary the way they are prepared.

To give you and your family time to adjust, avoid drastic changes. By making diet changes gradually, they are more likely to become a permanent part of your lifestyle.

For example, let's look at milk. Adults need two servings of milk group foods a day; the easiest way to get this is from two glasses of milk.

8-ounce Glass	Calories	Calories from Fat
Whole milk, 3.3 percent	150	72
Milk, 2 percent	120	45
Milk, 1 percent	100	27
Skim, 1/2 percent	90	less than 18

You get the same calcium, protein, and riboflavin benefits from each kind of milk, so why not try switching to one that helps promote better health. For instance, if you've been drinking whole milk, switch to two percent or switch to a mixture of half whole milk and half two percent, then switch to only two percent. Gradually get down to one percent or lower. It may take several months but, by making the adjustment slowly, you will be more likely to make the change a permanent one.

Often, persons who have done this say, "I don't like whole milk any more; it tastes like drinking cream."

The nutrients in milk remain essentially the same; all you remove are fat and calories.

If you're in the habit of putting a tablespoon of butter or margarine on a baked potato, you add 100 calories; two tablespoons of sour cream add another 50 calories. That's 150 calories entirely from fat, more calories than are in a plain five-ounce baked potato (138 calories if you eat skin and all). Slowly decrease the amount until you're adding little or no butter or margarine; try nonfat yogurt instead of sour cream. Or try broth or natural gravy from roasted lean meats with just a little margarine for flavor. Alternatively, serve the baked potato topped with vegetables such as mushrooms, broccoli or green peas.

Decrease the amount of fat you add when cooking vegetables. Suppose you normally add a half stick of margarine to a recipe of green beans. Gradually reduce the amount until you are adding only several teaspoons; you may not taste the difference. You might try diet margarine. Because it has water added, it contains only half the calories of regular margarine.

A piece of toast has seventy calories; spread it with two teaspoons of margarine and you've added seventy more calories, all from fat. Instead of margarine, add one teaspoon of low sugar jam and you add only eight calories; none of them from fat.

To break the habit of adding nondairy creamer to coffee, mix the creamer with nonfat dry milk in varying amounts until finally you are adding only milk. You will have done your body a favor by eliminating saturated fat from your coffee.

Use caution when adding fiber to your diet. Add high fiber foods gradually: the same property that helps fiber prevent constipation may provide too much of a laxative effect in some people.

So, make changes in the way you eat
...but gradually!

Getting Through the Morning

With busy schedules, even with the best intentions, healthy eating is often neglected. You skip a meal because you get rushed, or you reach for a candy bar because it's convenient. You miss breakfast only to pick up a donut and cup of coffee later. And if you have little or nothing for lunch, by dinner time, not only are you famished, but you give yourself permission to eat any and everything because you haven't eaten much throughout the day. This is definitely *not* the way to healthier living.

Plan to eat during the times of day you are most active. Eating a large meal in the evening and then relaxing the rest of the night tends to promote weight gain.

Just as you've heard many times, breakfast really is one of the most important meals of the day. For high energy levels to start your day, your body needs refueling. Without breakfast, blood sugar levels may fall below normal and that can make you tired, weak, irritable, and unable to concentrate long before lunch time. If you are unable to eat until you've been awake for several hours, think about taking a nutritious snack from home to eat at coffee break.

For breakfast, as for all meals, include foods from several food groups. For example, milk and cereal, or milk, fruit and toast. Foods from several groups combined at the same meal stay in the stomach longer than, say, if you just eat a piece of fruit. You may then resist the temptation to have a mid-morning donut or pastry.

If you are skipping breakfast because of lack of time, remember that many foods for breakfast can be prepared in a very few minutes. There is nothing wrong with heating leftovers from last night's casserole for your morning meal. Refrigerate leftovers overnight in a microwave safe dish. In the morning, heat and eat.

Another suggestion: make a breakfast drink in the blender with low-fat milk or yogurt, strawberries, and a banana. For variety, substitute fresh peaches or canned or fresh pineapple. Or, use orange juice, 1/4 to 1/3 cup nonfat dry milk and the fruit of your choice.

Try some of the quick-to-fix breakfast ideas below; each provides a wholesome meal when accompanied by fruit or fruit juice:

- **Dry cereal and low-fat milk.**

- **Bagel or whole wheat toast with part-skim ricotta cheese, sprinkled with raisins. Or omit the raisins, and lightly sprinkle with cinnamon and sugar.**

- **Toasted English muffin with a teaspoon of jelly or margarine, low-fat milk.**

- **English muffin with a slice of low-fat cheese. Heat in microwave oven 20 to 30 seconds to melt cheese.**

- **Oatmeal or bran muffin, low-fat milk .**

- **Graham crackers, low-fat milk.**

- **Quick-cooking oatmeal cooked in the bowl in a microwave oven. Follow directions on the box except use low-fat or skim milk in place of water for cooking. Add raisins, if desired. Instant oatmeal is satisfactory, but is higher in sodium.**

- **Nonfat or low-fat yogurt, whole wheat toast.**

Mid-Day Slump

The middle of the afternoon is the time energy starts to sag for many. What can you do about it? A light snack about 3 p.m. can help you get through the last few hours of the workday, especially if you neglected to eat lunch.

If you exercise or run errands instead of eating lunch, you *should* eat an afternoon snack. And make it a nutritious snack, not a candy bar. If you eat a candy bar, you get a quick rise in blood sugar. However, once your blood sugar rises, you get a quick spurt of insulin which creates a quick fall in blood sugar. When that happens, you are more hungry than when you started.

Of course, the best idea is to eat lunch. Your body works better when you feed it regularly. Lunch can be a sandwich brought from home or selected from the cafeteria. Choose tuna, turkey, lean roast beef and, occasionally, lean ham. Add lettuce and tomatoes, fresh fruit and milk and you have a healthy lunch. For a change, have yogurt, fresh fruit and crackers. If you have access to a refrigerator and microwave oven at work, try heating leftover casseroles or stews.

If some foods seem to make you sleepy after lunch, avoid them. Eating an unusually large lunch can also make you sleepy and may not be a good idea. If you meet with business associates, avoid the tendency to overindulge. To stay alert through the afternoon, eat a light lunch and plan to have a healthy snack if your energy sags. For ideas, read the information on snacks that starts on page 42.

Dinner

A relaxing dinner time can boost your physical and mental well being. No matter where you eat, strive to make it a pleasant occasion. Eat sitting down. Really taste the food and notice its texture. It takes a while for your brain to get the message that your stomach is full, so eat slowly. Quit eating when you are full—you don't *have* to clean your plate.

Think about what you've eaten during the day. Have you had two servings of milk group foods, two servings of meat or meat alternates, four servings of fruits and vegetables, and four servings of grains? Try to make up missing servings with your evening meal.

Dining at Home

When you plan your meal in advance and have the food on hand, you may find that cooking dinner is a pleasant way to unwind. Many of the entrees in the recipe section can be prepared in a short time.

Weekday dinner preparation can be simplified by cooking and freezing extra main dishes on the weekend, to be eaten during the week. Look in the recipe section for foods that are easy to cook in advance. After a hard day you will enjoy the convenience of having most of your evening meal already prepared. Just pop it into the microwave oven for quick heating while you set the table and make the salad.

Making your own frozen convenience main dishes may sound difficult, but is a habit worth acquiring. Freezing your own, rather than relying on packaged frozen dinners, will help you eat better and may save you money. If on occasion you purchase frozen dinners, select one that has fewer than thirty percent of its calories from fat and under 1000 milligrams of sodium.

Dining Out

On average, Americans eat out a little over three and one-half times a week. In 1987, we spent close to $200 billion eating at restaurants.* With an expenditure that large, we the customers can surely influence the kinds of food served at restaurants. If enough customers ask for healthier alternatives, eventually restaurant owners will get the message and offer healthier forms of food.

For the most part, it is up to you to select your food with care when eating out. The following are suggestions for some of the better choices. Do not hesitate to ask for substitutions for items not on the menu, such as baked potatoes instead of fried, or low-fat milk instead of nondairy creamer for your coffee. Remember, you are paying the bill.

Traditional Restaurant Dining

Avoid "all you can eat" restaurants.

If you plan to eat out on a special occasion and are counting your calories, try to eat a little less during the day.

Order "a la carte" if possible.

Take one roll and ask that the rolls and butter be removed from the table, or move them as far from you as possible.

For appetizers: order tomato juice, fruit, or have a clear broth or a clear vegetable soup.

Order baked, poached, roasted or broiled meats.

Remove skin from chicken, trim visible fat from meat.

---

*Tufts University Diet and Nutrition Newsletter, June 1987

Request vegetables without sauces.

Ask for salad dressing on the side and use only a small amount, or ask for oil and vinegar.

At a steak restaurant, choose a small filet mignon without bacon, a large salad with low calorie dressing or olive oil and vinegar. Have a plain baked potato with chives and a teaspoon or two of butter or sour cream.

In an Italian restaurant, skip the creamy white sauces. Select a pasta dish with a light tomato sauce that contains chicken or fish. Or, choose a simply prepared meat dish.

Chinese restaurants can be a good choice if you skip the wontons and eggrolls, and anything else deep fried. However, Chinese foods often contain large amounts of sodium; request your food be prepared with only a small amount of soy sauce and no MSG (monosodium glutamate). A stir-fry dish and rice is a good selection.

At a Mexican restaurant, order chicken fajitas with corn tortillas instead of flour tortillas and skip the sour cream and guacamole. Salsa is fine. Omit the refried beans since they generally have lard added; rice is a better choice.

Many cafeterias have an assortment of good choices such as baked or broiled fish, lean roast beef, plain vegetables, and vegetable or fruit salads without dressing. Desserts are often first in the cafeteria line to tempt you while you are hungry. Skip the dessert; go back for one after you've eaten only if you are still hungry.

If you have dessert, choose a fruit cup, fruit in liqueur, a fruit ice or sherbet, angel food cake, nonfat frozen yogurt, or ice milk.

Beverages, especially cocktails and soft drinks, can add many calories. A soft drink, one beer, 6 ounces of wine, or a 2-ounce cocktail provides about 150 calories. A light beer contains 100 calories. A wine spritzer (wine and club soda) contains 50 calories.

Water, black coffee or tea, diet sodas and club soda add no calories.

Fast-Food Restaurants

More than half the meals purchased outside the home come from fast-food restaurants. Every day one out of every five Americans eats in a fast-food restaurant. Many so-called "fast foods" contain large amounts of fat, sodium and calories. Health-conscious people try to avoid eating too many of these items, but time and convenience are also important considerations.

Can fast foods be a part of a healthy eating plan? If you make your selections with care, fast foods can be included in healthy eating. If you do end up with a meal that contains too much fat or sodium or too many calories, balance it with better selections the rest of the day. Listed below are some of the better choices.*

If you decide on hamburgers, buy the small size. Ask for mustard instead of mayonnaise. A small size fast food hamburger contains about 300 calories and 3 teaspoons of fat. (Some of the super size specials average 800 calories and 10 teaspoons of fat.) Order lettuce and tomatoes on your hamburger, and have a glass of low-fat milk and you've had an acceptable meal.

If pizza is your choice, buy plain cheese pizza topped with vegetables. Omit the olives, which are high in fat, as well as the meat. Thin crust pizza has fewer calories than thick crust pizza.

Look for a salad bar; choose a large assortment of vegetables with a small amount of turkey, chicken, tuna

---

* "The Fast-Food Guide" is an excellent paperback book about good and bad fast foods and how to tell the difference. Refer to the reading guide in the appendix.

or cheese. Add lemon juice or low calorie dressing. Avoid bacon bits and regular dressing.

Order a plain baked potato, add no more than 1 or 2 teaspoons of margarine or sour cream, or top with vegetables.

At a Mexican restaurant order a bean burrito that is not fried, or a tostada.

Skip the milkshakes, pies and croissants.

Have a small lean roast beef sandwich.

Avoid anything "breaded" or fried in deep fat.

Have low-fat or skim milk instead of a soft drink.

For breakfast, try pancakes with a small amount of syrup or jelly. Avoid the breakfast egg sandwiches, sausage and biscuts.

When Traveling on Business

Business travelers sometimes say, "I eat fine when I'm at home, but I can't eat right when I'm traveling." Admittedly, you may not be able to eat the way you would at home, but with some adjustments, you can improve your chances of getting a healthy meal.

Start when you make your airline reservation. Airline food can be very high in fat and calories, but most airlines provide alternatives to their regular meals at no extra charge. Request them when you make your reservation. Depending on the airline, you may have your choice of several low-fat, low-calorie alternatives. Do not drink alcohol on the plane; drink club soda instead. To compensate for the dry cabin air, drink a lot of water.

Do not skip any meals.

At a banquet, remove breading and skin from chicken, eat the vegetables and leave the sauces. Ask for lemon or oil and vinegar for your salad. Have a roll or two without butter and skip the rich desserts.

Drink more club soda than alcohol. Stay away from the peanuts. One mixed drink generally has 150 calories; 1/4 cup of peanuts has 210 calories. Club soda has no calories.

Follow the guidelines for dining out that start on page 29.

Vacation: Traveling by Car

Pack a lunch when possible. Include nutritious foods such as turkey or tuna sandwiches, carrot and celery sticks, and fresh fruit.

Bring along your own boxes of 100% fruit juices as an alternative to soft drinks.

Review the snack section starting on page 42 for other nutritious snack ideas.

Take a cooler to keep foods fresh and cold.

Buy additional ice, milk and fruits in local markets.

Think "healthy," follow these guidelines and you will have a good start on the road to healthier living.

Tips for Shopping and Cooking

Know Before You Go...

Shopping for food without planning ahead of time may result in impulse buying. Impulse buying can upset your resolve to buy only healthy foods and may wreck your food budget. By planning your menus in advance and making a list of what you will buy, you will eat healthier and may save money. It should also decrease shopping time.

An alternate planning method is to keep a running grocery list with general needs such as milk, cereal, several main dishes, foods for lunches and similar items. At the store, you then purchase a variety of foods based on the best buys, and plan your meals using these foods.

Proper planning will help you get maximum nutritional benefits for the time and effort you spend buying groceries and preparing meals. The following shopping and cooking tips will help in your planning.

Shopping

Try not to shop when hungry or with hungry children.

As much as possible, shop around the perimeter of the store, where fresh fruits and vegetables, breads, meats, and dairy products are found.

Cooking for one or two? Look in the supermarket produce department for broccoli and cauliflower florets. Or, buy fresh trimmed vegetables at the supermarket salad bar.

Many fresh vegetables lose nutritional value rapidly; buy only a few day's supply. Frozen and canned vegetables are packed at optimum maturity and may retain more nutrients than fresh produce stored too long.

To cut back on sodium, select low-salt or no-salt-added canned vegetables, soups, catsup and soy sauce.

Frozen orange juice is less expensive than fresh-squeezed, and just as nutritious.

Purchase peanut butter that has no added fat or sugar.

Look for canned fruits packed in unsweetened fruit juice or in extra light syrup.

For a low calorie jam or jelly, look for one that says "low sugar" instead of a fruit spread made without sugar. "Low sugar" fruit spreads contain 8 calories per teaspoon, while fruit spreads made without sugar contain 14 calories per teaspoon. Regular jam contains an average of 18 calories a teaspoon. Jams and jellies do not provide significant amounts of nutrients.

For less fat, buy tuna packed in water rather than in oil.

For a low calorie yogurt, buy nonfat plain yogurt and add your own fruit.

Purchase lean cuts of beef such as the bottom round, top round, or eye of the round steaks or roasts; this includes rump roasts and sirloin tip roast. Also sirloin steak, flank steak, beef tenderloin, lean stew meat, and extra lean ground beef.

For lean cuts of pork buy the loin, tenderloin, center-cut ham, or Canadian bacon.

For luncheon meats, look for those that contain no more than 2 grams of fat per ounce, such as turkey or chicken roll, turkey ham, turkey pastrami, or lean boiled ham.

These meats should be eaten in moderation since they usually have a large amount of salt added.

Some cheeses are very high in fat. The better choices are: part-skim ricotta or mozzarella cheese, low fat cottage cheese, farmer's skim milk cheese, and baker's cheese. Best selections are cheese products that have two grams or less of fat per ounce.

Exactly What Are You Buying?

Remember that ingredients are listed on a food label by descending order of weight; the item listed first is the most abundant.

Note that a product labeled "sugar free" does not necessarily mean you are not getting any sugar. According to the U.S. Food and Drug Administration regulations, a product labeled "sugar free" cannot contain sucrose (table sugar), but it may contain sugar in other forms. Read the ingredient list for words like corn solids, corn syrup, honey, glucose, maltose, dextrose, lactose or fructose: all are a form of sugar. Read labels for the words xylitol, sorbitol, and mannitol. These are sugar-related products that contain as many calories as sugar.

Read the ingredients on boxes of dry cereal. Look for breakfast cereals made with wheat germ and whole grains such as oats or wheat, bran, shredded wheat or wheat flakes. Some cereals contain over three teaspoons of sugar per serving. Besides sugar, many dry cereals contain a large amount of added fat and salt.

Select bread and crackers made from whole grain flours such as wheat, rye or oats. Some crackers contain a large amount of fat; read labels.

When purchasing whole wheat bread, read the ingredient list to see that only whole wheat flour is listed.

A product labeled wheat bread that includes wheat flour, enriched flour, or unbleached flour is not 100 percent whole wheat bread.

To get polyunsaturated cooking oil (the good kind of oil), purchase corn, safflower, sunflower seed, soybean, sesame seed, or cottonseed oil. Use low calorie mayonnaise or salad dressings made with these oils.

Avoid products that contain hydrogenated vegetable shortening, lard, beef tallow or fat, chicken fat, coconut oil and palm or palm kernel oil.

Buy a product with partially hydrogenated corn or soybean oils in preference to one with coconut or palm oil.

Assume cholesterol is in egg yolks, organ meats, fatty meats such as sausage, frankfurters, cold cuts and luncheon meats, _whole_ milk dairy products, butter and cream. Use these foods only occasionally.

A food can be labeled "no cholesterol" and still be a concentrated source of saturated fats (those most likely to raise blood cholesterol levels). Read lists of ingredients carefully.

A product labeled "100 percent vegetable shortening" may contain undesirable saturated oils like palm or coconut oil.

Purchase margarine that has liquid polyunsaturated oil listed as the first ingredient, or second if water is first, with at least twice as much polyunsatured fat as saturated.

If you buy prepared spaghetti sauce, look for one low in fat that contains acceptable oils such as olive, soybean or corn oil.

Are You Getting the Nutrition You're Paying For?

A nutrition label is provided on many products. This is different from the ingredient list. Read the nutrition label to know the value of what you are buying. The U. S. Food and Drug Administration (FDA) requires that any food to which a nutrient is added, or which makes a nutritional claim, must have a nutrition label. Nutrition labeling for other foods is optional.

A nutrition label lists the eight "leader" nutrients: protein, vitamin A, vitamin C, thiamine, riboflavin, niacin, calcium, and iron. The percentage beside each nutrient indicates how much of the U. S. Recommended Daily Allowance (RDA) is provided.

The U. S. RDA on food labels is based on body needs for most people in the United States over 4 years old. RDA's first were established by the Food and Nutrition Board of the National Academy of Sciences-National Research Council in 1943 and are revised as new research data becomes available. They are set at generous levels and provide a margin of safety for most people. This means you do not need exactly 100 percent of these requirements each day. If you consume close to the required amounts of the eight "leader" nutrients from a wide variety of foods, chances are you will get all the nutrients your body needs.

The nutrition label shows also the number of calories in a serving of the food, and lists by weight the amount of protein, carbohydrates, fat, and sodium. While not required by the FDA, a manufacturer may choose to list the amount of cholesterol.

Develop the habit of reading nutrition labels; they provide valuable information right at your fingertips.

Train yourself to check the fat content of all foods that come with a nutrition label, whether from the supermarket or from a vending machine. This is an important skill when you are monitoring the amount of fat you eat. (Ideally you want to consume thirty percent or fewer calories from fat.) Besides, it gets to be a fun habit and you can say, "Oh good, I'm taking care of myself."

To determine what percentage of calories in a serving of food come from fat:

Multiply the grams of fat by nine to get the number of calories from fat. Divide this by the total calories per serving to get the fraction of calories from fat in one serving. Multiply the result by 100 to get the percentage of calories from fat.

For example, suppose you are thinking of buying a can of chili con carne that contains 20 grams of fat and 300 total calories per serving. Calculate it this way:

$$\frac{20 \times 9}{300} \times 100 = 60 \text{ percent calories from fat}$$

That's twice the amount of fat you should be getting.

A way to picture the amount of fat in a serving of food is to convert the amount of fat to equivalent teaspoons. (Five grams of fat is the equivalent of one teaspoon.) For example, using the same chili con carne as above...

$$\frac{20}{5} = 4 \quad \text{or, twenty grams of fat is the equivalent of 4 teaspoons.}$$

Cooking Tips

Vitamins and minerals dissolve into vegetable cooking water, whether canned or fresh cooked. Plan to use the liquid in broths or soups.

To obtain more fiber in your diet, substitute whole wheat flour for up to half of the all-purpose flour when making bread, sauces, cookies, pancakes, or other recipes containing flour. Keep whole grain flour fresh by storing it in the refrigerator or freezer.

For maximum fiber, eat edible skins such as potato and apple skins, and seeds such as blackberry and summer squash seeds.

To increase calcium in your diet, sprinkle several tablespoons of nonfat dry milk in recipes such as meatloaf, puddings, soups, cookies, mashed potatoes and casseroles. Stir in an extra three tablespoons of nonfat dry milk anytime your recipe calls for 1 cup of flour.

You'll get significant amounts of calcium from canned sardines and canned salmon if you eat the bones. The soft bones mash easily and can be included in your recipe.

When making soup or stock with bones, add several tablespoons of vinegar to pull calcium from the bones into the soup.

Many recipes call for chopped onions and green peppers. Purchase them frozen and them keep on hand to use when time is at a premium, or freeze your own. Chop onions, spread them on a cookie sheet and freeze; place them in a freezer bag to use as needed. Do the same with green peppers.

To save time, purchase chopped fresh garlic in a jar.

Too much parsley? Wash and dry the parsley, chop and freeze it. Use it in cooking as you would fresh parsley.

Eggs are best stored in the refrigerater in their original carton. Eggs stored in the refrigerator door deteriorate quicker due to jarring when the door is opened and closed.

Egg whites separate easier from yolks when cold, but they beat better at room temperature. Adding cream of tarter helps them foam.

You may freeze extra egg whites but thaw them completely before using them.

Give extra egg yolks to your cat or dog; pets don't develop cholesterol problems.

When you cook, double the recipe, and freeze half for later use.

Use leftover drinking wine for cooking. It keeps well in the refrigerator.

When making soups or stews, chill after cooking and remove congealed fat from the top.

Dry salad greens after washing. Salad dressing clings better to dry greens, enabling you to use much less.

Olive oil may help lower cholesterol. Use extra-virgin olive oil in salads and vegetables when taste is important. It has a fruity olive flavor; a little will go a long way. Use one of the regular, less expensive olive oils for cooking.

When carving meats, use a sharp knife and cut the meat in very thin slices across the grain; several thin slices seems like more than one thick one. Meat which is cut across the grain seems more tender. This is important when using the lean cuts of meat that don't include a lot of fat.

Snacks

Americans are snacking more than ever. Growing teenagers seem to snack all the time. Younger children snack between meals because they can't eat a large enough volume of food in three meals a day to provide the nutrients their bodies need. Adults snack at social occasions, between meals, on breaks, and at bedtime. Sometimes a snack is eaten instead of a meal. As you may realize, foods eaten as snacks contribute a large percent of the calories many people eat each day.

The average person normally thinks of snack foods as soft drinks, potato chips, donuts, corn chips, cookies, and candy bars. Be aware that these contain a large proportion of fat, sodium, or calories, with almost no nutrients.

Sunflower seeds and nuts, favorite snack foods of many people, provide protein, some B-vitamins, and fiber, but are high in calories and fat. Hulled sunflower seeds and shelled dry roasted peanuts contain 160 calories per ounce; most other nuts contain around 200 calories per ounce. Cashews, macadamia nuts, and coconut contain large amounts of saturated fat and are to be avoided. In contrast, sunflower seeds and many nuts, including walnuts, pecans, almonds and peanuts, contain a high percentage of the more desirable fats.

With a little thought and planning, you can provide snacks for yourself and your family that make a positive contribution to a healthy body. Keep the empty calorie snack foods out of the house. If you must keep a few of the less desirable snacks on hand, put them in the freezer. Potato chips and corn chips freeze well, and the extra effort required to get them may turn out to be "too much trouble." Most children and adults will eat healthier snacks if they are readily available.

Look over the snack ideas that follow. You may decide to carry your own snack to work each day. For the occasions you end up at the vending machine, select better choices as indicated. If the vending machines do not contain the better choices, ask about having them provided.

Snacks particularly liked by youngsters include:

Dried fruits - nutritious but sweet and sticky. Try to
have children brush after eating this snack.

Prunes stuffed with peanut butter

Cube of low fat cheese and slice of banana on a pretzel
stick

Cube of low fat cheese on a carrot stick

Small slice of low fat cheese and crackers with unsalted
tops

Crunchy and brightly colored sliced raw vegetables served
with a dip of peanut butter, yogurt, or cottage cheese

Sliced or whole fruits - serve with peanut butter, cottage
cheese, yogurt, ricotta cheese, or milk. For example: a
wedge of apple spread with peanut butter.

Celery stuffed with peanut butter

Cereal mix - combine oat circles, wheat squares, peanuts,
pretzel sticks and raisins or diced fruit bits. Not for
very young children who might choke.

Graham crackers with peanut butter

Small sandwich

Small baked potato

Minibagels

Gelatin prepared with juice instead of water. Add diced
fruit.

Calorie controlled snack ideas for everyone:

Tomato juice

100 percent fruit juice

Fresh fruits

Fruit canned in juice or in extra light syrup

Low fat milk

Low fat buttermilk

Whole grain cereals or bread

English muffin

Bagel

Sliced raw vegetables

Plain popcorn popped without fat

Plain nonfat yogurt with unsweetened applesauce or diced fruit

Rice, wheat or corn cakes

Pretzels, unsalted

Crackers, unsalted tops

Whole grain crackers

Bread sticks

43

Snack ideas for those who can afford the calories:

Graham crackers
Dried fruits
Cookies made with oatmeal and whole grain flours
Oatmeal or bran muffins
Puddings made with skim milk
Ice milk
Sherbet
Low fat cheese and crackers
Banana or other fruit bread
A small sandwich made with tuna, turkey, lean roast beef, or peanut butter
Several tablespoons of sunflower seeds or peanuts
Slice of angel food cake
Vanilla wafers, ginger snaps, fig bars, animal crackers

Snacks from vending machines:

Choose	Avoid
Fruit	Cream-filled snacks
100% fruit juice	Soft drinks
Pretzels	Potato chips
Dry-roasted Almonds or peanuts	Corn chips
Vanilla wafers, ginger snaps, or shortbread cookies	Peanut butter crackers
Low-fat milk	Hot chocolate
Fig bars	Granola bar
Raisins	Candy bar

Nutrition and Stress *

It's simple chemistry. Understanding how the body responds to stress helps you understand the vital relationship between nutrition and stress. When the body is experiencing stress, the brain sends chemical messages or hormones such as adrenalin, throughout the body to help prepare for the "fight or flight response."

Your muscles tense; your heart rate increases; your breathing speeds up; your digestive system produces instant energy in the form of glucose and you are prepared to cope with any real or perceived danger that exists. In just a few seconds, you are ready to either meet the challenge or to withdraw rapidly—"the fight or flight response." When the stressful event has passed, your brain sends out another set of messages or hormones reversing the stress response and you will begin to physically relax.

Although this amazing response may have kept our ancestors from being devoured by sabre-tooth tigers, most of us today experience this same cycle in response to perceived threats rather than from genuine physical danger. If you believe you're in trouble, real or imagined, the stress response comes into play. Fighting with your spouse, being yelled at by your boss, nearly having a wreck will all trigger the same "fight or flight response." And because few of us stop to relax and to allow the body to return to normal, we keep our bodies at some level of the stress response nearly all the time.

Eating May Not Be the answer

When we're feeling blue, angry or bored, often it's easier to eat something than to think of an alternative to these unpleasant emotions. Certainly the media portrays eating a favorite food as the way to feel better in nearly any situation you might face. Yet many of the heavily advertised foods are the very foods that create more stress in our bodies!

---

* By Lynda Blakeslee, MSSW

Many of the foods we rely on during times of stress or fatigue may actually cause us more stress. When these foods are digested they become chemical signals that trigger the stress response.

Foods like alcohol and sugar may have an immediate effect that is pleasant or desirable such as relaxation or increased energy, but when consumed in excess they can reduce your body's ability to withstand stress.

Caffeine is a stimulant that produces the "fight or flight response" in your body. Coffee, tea, chocolate and colas are high in caffeine. Drink them only in moderate amounts. Substitute instead herbal teas, decaffeinated coffee or tea, or warm water.

Eating as stress management is only a temporary distraction from the source of your problems. Like using alcohol, the initial effect may be pleasant but this type of eating pattern may soon become a major source of stress in your life.

To Decrease Stress

A poor diet contributes to a poor reaction to stress. When you are under stress, your need for nutrients increases, especially your need for calcium and the B vitamins.

Feeling fatigued, nervous and irritable? The answer may be in eating a balanced diet and relaxation exercises instead of expensive therapy.

Explore some different options for dealing with your less positive moods. Remember that it's normal to have times when you are bored or tired or angry. If these times occur frequently or interfere with your relationships, consider getting professional assistance or counseling to help you find new strategies for dealing with these emotions.

What About Exercise? ═══════════

Most people should exercise at least three or four times a week for approximately 30 minutes, according to many experts. Exercise can make you look better and feel better, and may help you to live longer. And whether you want to lose weight or gain weight, exercise may be the equalizer you need.

To Help You Lose Weight

Many health problems are linked to obesity, and much of the obesity in our country is linked to inactivity. If you are overweight, exercise can help you lose weight and control your weight. To lose weight you must create a calorie deficit; that is, you must burn more calories than you take in. Two of the best ways to create that deficit are to decrease food intake and to add exercise. Look for opportunities to add exercise in your everyday activities. You might take the stairs instead of the elevator, park a little farther away in the parking lot, or sweep the walk at home.

It takes a deficit of 3,500 calories to lose one pound of fat. If you decrease your food calories by 500 per day for seven days, you will probably lose one pound. On the other hand, if you add a daily exercise expenditure of 250 calories, you will have to eliminate only 250 food calories to lose the same amount. In addition, adding exercise will help muscle tone and give you a feeling of accomplishment.

Besides stepping up daily activities, add an aerobic exercise. An aerobic exercise is one which results in a faster heart rate and heavier breathing than your usual everyday activity. Metabolism is accelerated; you burn calories at a faster rate both during the exercise and for some time afterward. Brisk walking, swimming, bicy-

47

cling, jogging, and programmed aerobics are all good. To expend 250 calories, a 150 pound person might choose to walk briskly for fifty minutes, bicycle for an hour, or jog for half an hour.

Will all this exercise make you hungry? Your appetite will not increase unless you exercise to excess, because you will be using stored fat. Keep in mind that to burn fat, an exercise needs to be done in 20-minute or longer increments, three or four times a week.

Start an exercise program slowly. Some people may have a condition that would be aggravated by the wrong kind of exercise. If you are seriously overweight or if you have not exercised in a long while, check with your doctor before beginning an exercise program.

To Help You Gain Weight

According to the President's Council on Physical Fitness, if you are a lean person in good condition, exercise may increase your appetite. It is possible the exercise may also burn up the extra calories consumed. To gain weight, continue to exercise and increase the number of calories you take in.

"The Bottom Line"

Whether or not you are satisfied with the shape of your body, you need exercise. The important thing is to pick an exercise you like so you will stay with it. Regular exercise can help you work better, play better, sleep better and feel better. And, according to the President's Council on Physical Fitness, it will make you more resistant to the degenerative diseases of middle and later life, especially diseases of the heart and blood vessels.

MEATS & MAIN DISHES

Many of the recipes in this section are everyday dishes revised to contain less meat and more complex carbohydrates. This revision does not diminish the tastiness of the dish; it still maintains the meaty flavor that most people enjoy. Most have less fat than the original recipe. From a study of these recipes you may get ideas about how to change your family favorites.

Recipes that include soy sauce contain the most sodium. Serve these dishes over rice prepared with no added salt.

Sloppy Joes

1/2 pound extra lean
    ground beef
1 (15 ounce) can
    no-salt-added
    stewed tomatoes
1 (16 ounce) can
    navy beans, rinsed
    and drained
1/4 cup catsup
1/4 teaspoon
    oregano leaves
1/8 teaspoon
    black pepper

5 hamburger buns

Cook ground beef in a 2-quart microwave safe dish on full power for 3 to 4 minutes until meat is no longer pink.

Stir once while cooking, breaking up any chunks of meat. Drain fat.

Add stewed tomatoes, breaking up the large pieces with a spoon.

Stir in remaining ingredients except hamburger buns.

Cook uncovered on full power 8 to 10 minutes until mixture thickens and is heated through, stirring once or twice.

To serve, spoon over hamburger buns.

Makes 5 servings.

Tips...

Optional: Add 1 to 2 tablespoons oatmeal to thicken the mixture.

Serve with cooked cauliflower or carrots and baked apple slices.

Extra sloppy joe mixture may be frozen.

Analysis: (Each serving, including the bun)

Calories	325
Total Fat	7.2 grams
Saturated Fat	2.3 grams
Monounsat. Fat	2.6 grams
Polyunsat. Fat	1.1 grams
Cholesterol	28 mgs
Sodium	598 mgs

50

Spaghetti Squash with Meat Sauce ⎯⎯⎯

**3/4 pound extra
    lean ground beef**
**1 large onion,
    chopped fine**
2 carrots, chopped fine
1 rib celery, chopped fine
1 clove garlic, minced
**1 (15-ounce) can
    tomato sauce**
1/4 cup water
1 bay leaf
**1/2 teaspoon
    oregano leaves**
1/2 teaspoon basil leaves
1/2 teaspoon salt
1/4 teaspoon pepper

**4 cups cooked spaghetti
    squash**

**2 tablespoons shredded
    Parmesan cheese**

Cook ground beef 3-4 minutes in a 2-quart casserole, on full power. Drain fat.

Add onion, carrots, celery, and garlic; combine well. Cover and cook 8 minutes longer, or until vegetables are soft; stir several times while cooking.

Add remaining ingredients, except Parmesan cheese and squash. Cook, covered, on full power 5 minutes, then at half power 15 minutes. If sauce is too thick, add additional water.

To serve, place spaghetti squash on a platter and pour meat sauce over. Sprinkle with Parmesan cheese.

Makes 6 servings

Tips... ⎯⎯⎯⎯⎯⎯⎯⎯⎯⎯⎯⎯

Serve with broccoli or green beans, celery sticks and whole wheat toast.

A good recipe for waist watchers.

Sauce may be used as regular spaghetti sauce.

You may substitute ground turkey for the beef.

Leftovers freeze well.

Analysis: (Each serving,
    includes 2/3 cup squash)

Calories	198
Total Fat	8.3 grams
Saturated Fat	2.9 grams
Monounsat. Fat	3.0 grams
Polyunsat. Fat	0.6 grams
Cholesterol	42 mgs
Sodium	710 mgs

Mexican One Dish Meal

1 pound extra lean
    ground beef or
    ground turkey
1 small onion, chopped
1 clove garlic, minced
1 green pepper, diced
2 medium potatoes, diced
1 (8-ounce) can tomato
    sauce
2 cans (2 cups) water
2 teaspoons chili powder
1/2 teaspoon salt
1/4 teaspoon cumin
1/4 teaspoon
    black pepper
1 (12-ounce) can whole
    kernel corn, drained

Cook ground beef or turkey and onion in large non-stick skillet. Stir occasionally while cooking.

When meat is lightly browned and onion is soft, drain off fat. Add all remaining ingredients except corn.

Cover, and simmer over low heat, stirring occasionally, until potatoes are tender, about 30 minutes. Add more water if needed.

Add corn; cook long enough to heat through.

Makes 6 servings.

Tips...

You may omit the corn.

Serve with raw carrot and celery sticks.

Scrub the potatoes well, but do not peel.

Analysis: (Each serving, using beef)

Calories	270
Total Fat	9.3 grams
Saturated Fat	3.3 grams
Monounsat. Fat	3.9 grams
Polyunsat. Fat	0.6 grams
Cholesterol	54 mgs
Sodium	610 mgs

Easy Meat Loaf

1 pound ground round, or extra lean ground beef
1/4 cup dry bread crumbs
2/3 cup evaporated skim milk, undiluted
3 tablespoons instant minced onion
1/2 teaspoon salt
1/4 teaspoon pepper
1/4 cup catsup

Combine all ingredients except catsup.

Shape mixture into loaf in baking dish.

Cook 40 minutes at 350-degrees.

Spread catsup over top and cook 15 minutes longer.

Makes 4 servings.

❖ *Alternate MICROWAVE cooking instructions:*

Form meat mixture into a donut shape in a microwave-safe shallow baking dish.

Cook at medium-high appoximately 14 minutes, give dish 1/2 turn half way through cooking time. Spread catsup over top during the last few minutes of cooking.

For 500 watt microwave ovens, cook on full power.

Tips...

Serve with baked potatoes, zucchini squash, and a combination salad.

No egg is needed in this meat loaf. The milk and bread crumbs bind it together.

Meat loaf freezes well after baking.

Forty-one percent of the calories in this recipe come from fat. Add only one teaspoon of butter or margarine to your baked potato and the percentage is less than thirty for the meal. Try non-fat yogurt and green onion or chives on your potato.

Analysis: (Each serving)

Calories	300
Total Fat	13.5 grams
Saturat. Fat	5.0 grams
Monounsat. Fat	5.8 grams
Polyunsat. Fat	0.6 grams
Cholesterol	83 mgs
Sodium	561 mgs

Beef Strips in Tomato Sauce

1 pound boneless sirloin, cut in strips 1/2x1/8x2-inches
1 clove garlic, minced
1 tablespoon vegetable oil
1 onion, chopped
1 (14 1/2-ounce) can stewed tomatoes
1 green pepper, thinly sliced
1/2 cup beef broth
1 tablespoon cornstarch
1/2 teaspoon dried basil leaves
1/2 teaspoon dried oregano
1/4 teaspoon salt
1/4 teaspoon pepper

4 cups hot cooked spaghetti (8 ounces uncooked)

Trim fat from beef before cutting into strips.

In large non-stick skillet or wok, over medium-high heat, cook beef and garlic in hot oil, stirring often until beef changes color. Add onion and continue to cook until onion begins to soften.

Stir in tomatoes and green pepper. Combine remaining ingredients except spaghetti and add to meat mixture.

Cook 2 or 3 minutes longer, until gravy thickens slightly.

Cover. Simmer over low heat for 15 minutes, stirring occasionally.

Meanwhile, cook spaghetti as package directs. Drain.

Serve beef strips over hot cooked spaghetti.

Makes 5 servings.

Tips...

Sprinkle with Parmesan cheese, if desired. Add a tossed green salad and crusty bread to complete the meal.

Recipe freezes well.

A good quality top round steak may be substituted for the sirloin.

Analysis: (Each serving, includes 3/4 cup of spaghetti)

Calories	371
Total Fat	9.6 grams
Saturated Fat	3.0 grams
Monounsat. Fat	3.5 grams
Polyunsat. Fat	2.3 grams
Cholesterol	61 mgs
Sodium	520 mgs

Beef Strogonoff

1 pound boneless sirloin	Trim fat from beef; slice beef into thin strips, about 2 inches long.
1 tablespoon vegetable oil	
1 cup thinly sliced onions	
1 garlic clove, minced	Heat oil in a large nonstick skillet.
2 cups thinly sliced mushrooms	Add beef and cook over high heat until meat is lightly browned; add onions, garlic and mushrooms. Cook over medium heat until onions are soft. Remove from heat.
1/4 cup flour	
1/4 cup chopped parsley	
1/4 teaspoon salt	
1/4 teaspoon pepper	Stir in flour, parsley, salt and pepper. Gradually add beef broth and tomato paste. Cook over medium heat until mixture comes to a boil and thickens. Remove from heat.
1 cup beef broth	
2 tablespoons tomato paste	
1 tablespoon cornstarch	
2/3 cup nonfat yogurt	In a small bowl, mix the cornstarch with 2 tablespoons of yogurt, then stir in remaining yogurt.

Stir yogurt into meat mixture; simmer over low heat 3 to 4 minutes.

If mixture is too thick, add additonal broth.

Makes 6 servings

Tips...

Adding cornstarch to the yogurt helps stabilize it to prevent curdling.

Serve over hot cooked noodles accompanied by asparagus, combination salad and crusty bread.

Analysis: (Each serving)

Calories	200
Total Fat	7.5 grams
Saturated Fat	2.5 grams
Monounsat. Fat	2.9 grams
Polyunsat. Fat	1.7 grams
Cholesterol	52 mgs
Sodium	323 mgs

Stir-Fry Pepper Steak

1 tablespoon oil
1 pound boneless sirloin,
cut in strips 1/8" x 2"
2 gloves garlic, minced
1 teaspoon minced
gingerroot, optional
1 onion, thinly sliced
3 large green peppers,
cut in thin strips

Seasoning Sauce:
1 cup beef broth
2 tablespoons soy
sauce
2 tablespoons
rice wine vinegar
1 tablespoon cornstarch
1/2 teaspoon sugar
1/4 teaspoon
black pepper

2 1/2 cups hot cooked rice

Combine seasoning sauce ingredients in a small bowl; reserve.

Heat oil in large skillet or wok over high heat. Add beef, garlic and gingerroot; cook, stirring and turning meat continously, until meat is lightly browned.

Add onion, and stir fry about a minute.

Add green peppers; cook and stir 3 minutes, or until peppers are crispy tender.

Stir the seasoning sauce, and add it to the meat mixture in the skillet.

Cook and stir until mixture boils and gravy thickens slightly, about 2 minutes. Serve over rice.

Makes 5 servings.

Tips...

Serve with fruit cup of diced fresh fruit.

Beef with Peppers & Tomatoes:

Use only 1 green pepper. Add 2 tomatoes cut in 8 wedges each when you add the seasoning sauce.

Beef with Broccoli:

Use pepper steak recipe. Omit green pepper. Add 3 to 4 cups cut-up broccoli. Add water chestnuts if desired.

Analysis: (Each serving, includes 1/2 cup rice.)

Calories	328
Total Fat	9.1 grams
Saturated Fat	3.0 grams
Monounsat. Fat	3.5 grams
Polyunsat. Fat	2.1 grams
Cholesterol	61 mgs
Sodium	562 mgs

Texas Beef Stew

1/4 cup flour
2 cups water
1/4 cup plus
   2 tablespoons
   catsup
1 1/2 tablespoons
   lemon juice
1 pound bottom
   round steak,
   trimmed, and cut
   into cubes
4 small potatoes
4 small carrots
4 small onions
1/4 teaspoon pepper

Blend together flour and 1/2 cup water in dutch oven or large heavy-duty saucepan.

Stir in remaining water, catsup, and lemon juice.

Cook, stirring constantly, over high heat until mixture is thickened.

Add remaining ingredients; bring to a boil.

Reduce heat; simmer stew for 2 to 2 1/2 hours until meat is tender and vegetables are done.

Makes 4 servings.

Tips...

*Serve with sliced fresh
tomatoes and whole wheat
toast.*

*Leftover stew may be
frozen if potatoes are
removed; potatoes become
mushy when frozen.*

Analysis: (Each serving)

Calories	379
Total Fat	8.3 grams
Saturated Fat	2.8 grams
Monounsat. Fat	3.4 grams
Polyunsat. Fat	0.5 grams
Cholesterol	75 mgs
Sodium	308 mgs

Beef and Bean Stew

1 (8-ounce) can
    tomato sauce
2 tablespoons flour
1 tablespoon
    prepared mustard
2 teaspoons chili powder
    or to taste
1 teaspoon brown sugar
1/2 teaspoon salt
1 1/2 pounds bottom
    round steak, trimmed,
    cut into cubes
3/4 cup water
1 large onion,
    cut in 6 wedges
1 (15-ounce) can
    kidney beans
	In dutch oven or heavy duty saucepan, combine tomato sauce with the flour, mustard, chili powder, sugar, and salt. Blend well.
	
	Stir in meat and water.
	
	Bring to a boil over medium-high heat, stirring frequently.
	
	Reduce heat, cover, and cook slowly 1 1/2 hours, stirring occasionally.
	
	Add onions and beans and continue cooking, covered, 30 minutes, or until meat is tender.
	
	Makes 8 servings

Tips...

Serve over brown or white rice with sliced raw carrots and crusty bread.

It is not necessary to drain the kidney beans unless you want a thicker stew.

Prepared stew freezes well.

Analysis: (Each serving)

Calories	227
Total Fat	7.0 grams
Saturated Fat	2.2 grams
Monounsat. Fat	2.8 grams
Polyunsat. Fat	0.5 grams
Cholesterol	60 mgs
Sodium	585 mgs

Swiss Steak

1 (2-pound) full cut round steak, 1/2-inch thick	Preheat broiler unit in range.
3 tablespoons flour	Cut round steak along natural separations; trim all visible fat and connective tissue. Cut into serving size pieces.
1/2 teaspoon salt	
1/4 teaspoon black pepper	Coat meat with a mixture of the flour, salt and pepper.
1 (14-ounce) can tomatoes, drained	
1 large onion, chopped	Spray bottom of 13 x 9-inch pan with vegetable cooking spray. Place steak in pan.
1 green pepper, diced	Position pan so top of meat is 4 or 5 inches from heating element.

1 (2-pound) full cut round steak, 1/2-inch thick
3 tablespoons flour
1/2 teaspoon salt
1/4 teaspoon black pepper
1 (14-ounce) can tomatoes, drained
1 large onion, chopped
1 green pepper, diced

Preheat broiler unit in range.

Cut round steak along natural separations; trim all visible fat and connective tissue. Cut into serving size pieces.

Coat meat with a mixture of the flour, salt and pepper.

Spray bottom of 13 x 9-inch pan with vegetable cooking spray. Place steak in pan. Position pan so top of meat is 4 or 5 inches from heating element.

Brown steak, top side only, for 5 to 7 minutes. Check often after the first 5 minutes to see that it doesn't burn.

Remove pan from oven; set oven temperature at 350-degrees.

Add remaining ingredients to meat, cover with aluminum foil, and bake at 350-degrees 1 1/2 to 2 hours or until meat is tender.

Makes 8 servings.

Tips...

Serve with baked potatoes, a green vegetable, and a combination salad without tomatoes.

Use sauce from the cooked steak to season the baked potato.

Bake potatoes in the oven at the same time meat is cooking.

Analysis: (Each serving)

Calories	206
Total Fat	8.3 grams
Saturated Fat	2.7 grams
Monounsat. Fat	3.4 grams
Polyunsat. Fat	0.4 grams
Cholesterol	75 mgs
Sodium	235 mgs

Rump Roast Italian Style

1 (3 pound) boneless
    rump roast
1 tablespoon
    vegetable oil
1 large onion, chopped
1 can (15-ounce)
    tomato sauce
3 ounces tomato paste
    (1/2 of a
    6-ounce can)
1 carrot,
    coarsely chopped
1 rib celery,
    coarsely chopped
1/2 cup dry red wine
1/2 cup water
1/4 teaspoon salt
1/4 teaspoon pepper
1/8 teaspoon marjoram
Dash thyme leaves
1/2 pound fresh
    mushrooms, sliced

Trim fat from meat. Brown meat in large heavy-duty saucepan in hot oil over medium-high heat. Add onion and cook until onion softens.

Add remaining ingredients, except mushrooms, and bring to a boil.

Reduce heat and simmer meat, covered, for 2 1/2 to 3 hours or until meat is very tender when pierced with a fork. Turn the meat and baste with pan juices every thirty minutes. Add mushrooms after meat has cooked about 2 hours.

Thinly slice the meat, place on a warm platter, and spoon several tablespoons of gravy over the meat. Serve immediately.

Makes 11 servings.

Tips...

Sauce from the meat may be served over macaroni as a side dish along with green peas, combination salad (no tomatoes), and French or Italian bread.

Select an evenly shaped rump roast. Trim fat before cooking.

Extra tomato paste freezes well.

Slice extra roast, cover with gravy and freeze in meal-size portions.

Analysis: (Each serving)

Calories	229
Total Fat	9.5 grams
Saturated Fat	2.9 grams
Monounsat. Fat	3.7 grams
Polyunsat. Fat	1.2 grams
Cholesterol	75 mgs
Sodium	419 mgs

Stir-Fry Pork over Spaghetti

1/2 pound
  pork tenderloin
1 clove garlic, minced
1/2 tablespoon oil
2 cups cut-up broccoli
1/2 cup red or
  green pepper,
  cut in 1-inch pieces
1 cup mushrooms, sliced

Seasoning Sauce:
  3/4 cup low-sodium
  chicken broth
1 tablespoon
  cornstarch
2 tablespoons
  soy sauce
2 tablespoons
  dry sherry

2 cups hot cooked
  spaghetti (4-ounces
  uncooked)

Combine seasoning sauce ingredients; reserve. Slice pork tenderloin in thin slices approximately 1/8-inch thick.

Add garlic to meat. Heat oil over high heat in a non-stick skillet or wok. Add meat and stir and turn continuously until meat is brown and done through.

Add vegetables; stir and cook 2 minutes.

Blend seasoning sauce before adding it to skillet.

Bring all to a boil, lower heat, and simmer 3 minutes, stirring occasionally.

Meanwhile, cook spaghetti according to package directions.

Serve the pork and vegetables over the hot spaghetti.

Makes 3 servings.

Tips...

Instead of the fresh vegetables, you may use 2 1/4 cups (half of a 1-pound package) of frozen combination vegetables, such as the broccoli, red pepper, bamboo shoot, and mushroom mixture.

Serve over rice instead of spaghetti, if you prefer.

Carrot and raisin salad or diced fresh fruit cup completes the meal.

Analysis: (Each serving, includes 2/3 cup spaghetti)

Calories	335
Total Fat	6.5 grams
Saturated Fat	1.6 grams
Monounsat. Fat	2.2 grams
Polyunsat. Fat	2.2 grams
Cholesterol	59 mgs
Sodium	665 mgs

Cajun Pork and Rice

1/2 pound pork loin,
   cut in thin strips
1/2 tablespoon
   vegetable oil
1 rib celery, thinly sliced
1/2 cup diced green
   pepper
2 green onions cut in
   1/4-inch slices
1 clove garlic, minced
1 1/4 cups chicken broth
1/4 cup white wine
1/2 cup rice
1/4 teaspoon salt
1/4 teaspoon cumin
1/4 teaspoon thyme
Dash cayenne pepper,
   or to taste

Trim visible fat from meat. In a skillet over medium-high heat, cook the meat in hot oil, stirring often until meat is lightly browned.

Add the celery, green pepper, onions, and garlic; cook and stir 1 or 2 minutes longer.

Stir in remaining ingredients, bring to a boil. Cover and simmer 20 minutes, or until rice is tender.

Makes 3 servings.

Tips...

You may omit the wine and add an additional 1/4 cup of chicken broth.

Serve with broccoli and fresh fruit cup of 1 orange, 1 apple and 1 banana.

Analysis: (Each serving)

Calories	309
Total Fat	10.1 grams
Saturated Fat	2.7 grams
Monounsat. Fat	3.7 grams
Polyunsat. Fat	2.4 grams
Cholesterol	59 mgs
Sodium	569 mgs

Ham Fried Rice

1 tablespoon vegetable oil
3 ounces lean cured ham, diced (about 1/2 cup)
1/2 cup chopped onion
1/2 cup diced green pepper
3 cups cold cooked rice
1/2 cup frozen peas, thawed
1/4 cup low-sodium chicken broth
1 tablespoon soy sauce
1 tablespoon rice wine vinegar
1/2 teaspoon sugar
1/4 teaspoon black pepper
1 whole egg plus 1 egg white

Heat oil in wok or large skillet over medium-high heat.

Add ham, onion, and green pepper; stir and fry 2 to 3 minutes, until onion begins to soften.

Add rice and peas. Cook and stir 3 to 4 minutes or until heated through.

Add broth, soy sauce, vinegar, sugar and pepper.

Beat together the egg plus the egg white; add to rice mixture. Stir and cook until eggs are done.

Makes 4 servings.

Tips...

Serve with baked tomatoes, diced fresh fruit, and whole wheat toast.

Substitute green onions cut in 1/4-inch pieces for the regular onion. You may add diced water chestnuts and/or leftover cooked vegetables instead of the peas. Cooked brown rice may be substituted for white rice.

Shrimp Fried Rice:

Subsitute 1 (4 1/2-ounce) can shrimp, rinsed and drained, for the ham. Add shrimp after adding rice.

Analysis: (Each serving)

Calories	290
Total Fat	6.8 grams
Saturated Fat	1.4 grams
Monounsat. Fat	2.1 grams
Polyunsat. Fat	2.6 grams
Cholesterol	65 mgs
Sodium	559 mgs

Pasta Primavera

1 cup evaporated skim
milk
2/3 cup grated Parmesan
cheese, divided
2-ounces (1/2 cup grated)
part-skim
mozzarella cheese
1 teaspoon basil leaves
1/2 teaspoon oregano
1/2 teaspoon black pepper
1 tablespoon vegetable oil
1 onion, chopped
1/4 pound lean cured
ham, diced
(about 2/3 cup)
1 (1-pound) package
frozen broccoli,
cauliflower,
carrot combination,
thawed and drained

4 cups cooked fettuccini
(8 ounces uncooked)

Combine milk, 1/3 cup Parmesan cheese, mozzarella cheese, basil, oregano, and pepper. Let sit at room temperature while preparing remainder of recipe.

Heat oil in a large non-stick skillet over medium heat; add onion and cook until onion is soft. Cut any large pieces of vegetables to bite size. Add vegetables and ham to skillet; cook until heated through.

Meanwhile cook fettuccini according to package directions. To the cooked, drained pasta, add the ham and vegetable mixture and the cheese mixture.

Mix well, sprinkle remaining Parmesan cheese over top and serve immediately.

Makes 6 servings.

Tips...

To thaw vegetables, heat on full power in microwave oven 3 to 5 minutes.

For a spicier taste, add a few drops of tabasco sauce or a small amount of crushed red pepper.

Fettuccini is a type of pasta about 1/4-inch wide.

To complete the meal, add sliced fresh tomatoes and crusty bread.

This recipe provides more than one third of an adult's daily calcium requirement.

Analysis: (Each serving)

Calories	325
Total Fat	9.6 grams
Saturated Fat	4.1 grams
Monounsat. Fat	2.7 grams
Polyunsat. Fat	1.8 grams
Cholesterol	26 mgs
Sodium	595 mgs

Spaghetti with Fresh Tomatoes & Ham

2 tablespoons olive oil
2 cloves garlic
1/4 pound lean cured
  ham, diced (about
  2/3 cup)
1 onion, chopped
1/4 cup dry white wine
1 pound tomatoes
  (3 medium),
  peeled and diced
1/4 cup chopped parsley
1/2 teaspoon salt
1/2 teaspoon
  black pepper

1 pound spaghetti
1 1/2 tablespoons
  margarine, melted

1/2 cup grated Parmesan
  cheese

Heat oil over medium heat in a large skillet. Add garlic; cook until golden.

Discard garlic. Add ham and onion. Cook until onion is soft.

Add wine; boil about one minute.

Add tomatoes, salt and pepper. Cook over medium-high heat for only 5 minutes, so tomatoes retain their fresh taste. Add parsley during the last minute of cooking.

Meanwhile cook spaghetti according to package directions, until tender but firm to the bite. Drain spaghetti and coat with margarine. Place in warm bowl.

Pour sauce over spaghetti; sprinkle with cheese, and serve immediately.

Makes 6 servings.

Tips...

Reserve several tablespoons of spaghetti water to add if you want a juicier sauce.

Serve with pickled beets, a green salad, and crusty white bread.

Analysis: (Each serving)

Calories	424
Total Fat	12.6 grams
Saturated Fat	3.3 grams
Monounsat. Fat	6.1 grams
Polyunsat. Fat	2.1 grams
Cholesterol	18 mgs
Sodium	649 mgs

Veal Scaloppine with Marsala Wine ___

1 pound veal scallops, thinly sliced
2 tablespoons flour
1/2 teaspoon salt
1/4 teaspoon black pepper
1/2 tablespoon margarine
1/2 tablespoon olive oil
1/3 cup Marsala wine
1/2 cup chicken broth
2 tablespoons chopped parsley

2 cups hot cooked rice (2/3 cup uncooked)

Combine flour, salt, and pepper. Coat veal pieces with flour mixture; shake off excess so that not much flour remains on them.

Heat margarine and oil in a large non-stick skillet.

Brown veal over medium-high heat. As meat browns, remove pieces to a warm platter.

Add wine and chicken broth to skillet. Bring to a boil. Cook 1 or 2 minutes.

Return veal to skillet. Simmer until sauce thickens slightly, about 5 minutes.

Place rice on warm platter. Place meat over rice; pour sauce over.

Sprinkle parsley over all.

Makes 4 servings

Tips... ___

Use dry Marsala wine, not the sweet Marsala.

Serve with a green vegetable like green beans, a combination salad, and Italian bread.

Chicken Marsala:

Use chicken breasts, boned and skinned instead of veal. Pound to about 1/4-inch thickness.

Veal with Lemon Sauce:

Follow above recipe. Instead of wine, use 3 tablespoons of fresh lemon juice.

Analysis: (Each serving, includes 1/2 cup rice)

Calories	356
Total Fat	11.8 grams
Saturated Fat	4.4 grams
Monounsat. Fat	5.8 grams
Polyunsat. Fat	1.3 grams
Cholesterol	79 mgs
Sodium	432 mgs

POULTRY

Always wash chicken before you cook it. Any utensil or cutting board used for preparing chicken should be washed before being used for any other food preparation.

Cook chicken until the juices run clear when pricked with a fork; do not eat chicken that is not cooked through.

Many of the recipes in this section call for boned and skinned chicken breasts. Besides being low in fat, chicken breasts combine well with other ingredients to provide a wide range of flavors.

Chinese Chicken

1/2 tablespoon oil

1/2 pound boneless, skinless chicken breasts cut in thin slivers

1 small onion, chopped

2 1/4 cups frozen broccoli, baby carrots, water chestnut combination, partially thawed (1/2 of a 1-pound package)

3/4 cup low sodium chicken or beef broth

1 1/2 tablespoons soy sauce

2 teaspoons cornstarch

Heat oil in non-stick skillet or wok.

Add chicken and onion; stir and cook over high heat until chicken is lightly browned.

Combine cornstarch with soy sauce and broth; add to skillet along with the vegetables. Bring to a boil.

Cover and simmer 3 to 5 minutes or until vegetables are tender.

Makes 3 servings.

Tips...

Serve over hot cooked rice. Add fruit and your meal is complete.

This recipe, like many stir-fry recipes, is one you can vary to use ingredients you have on hand. Beef, ham, or pork may be used as well as a wide assortment of vegetables. Always include the onion; it adds a lot of flavor. 1/4 teaspoon of instant minced garlic and several tablespoons dry sherry or white wine will also add flavor.

Analysis: (Each serving)

Calories	175
Total Fat	4.9 grams
Saturated Fat	1.0 grams
Monounsat. Fat	1.5 grams
Polyunsat. Fat	2.0 grams
Cholesterol	49 mgs
Sodium	596 mgs

Chicken Ratatouille

1 tablespoon
   vegetable oil
1 pound boneless
   chicken breasts, cut
   in 1-inch pieces
2 small zucchini squash,
   thinly sliced but
   not peeled
1 small eggplant,
   about 3/4 pound,
   peeled and
   cut in 1-inch cubes
1 large onion,
   thinly sliced
1 medium green
   pepper, cut in
   1-inch pieces
1/2 pound mushrooms,
   sliced
1 (15-ounce) can
   tomato wedges

1/2 teaspoon instant
   minced garlic
1 teaspoon basil leaves
1 teaspoon parsley flakes
1/2 teaspoon salt
1/2 teaspoon black pepper

Heat oil in a 12-inch nonstick skillet or heavy duty saucepan. Cook chicken over medium-high heat, stirring often, until lightly browned.

Add zucchini, eggplant, onion, green pepper and mushrooms.

Cook, uncovered, over medium heat stirring occasionally until vegetables are tender crisp, about 15 minutes.

Add remaining ingredients, stirring gently so as not to break up tomatoes. Cook about 5 minutes longer.

Makes 4 servings.

Tips...

Serve with hot steamed white or brown rice, raw carrot sticks, and rye bread.

This recipe was adapted from a winning recipe in a national chicken contest several years ago.

Analysis: (Each serving)

Calories	253
Total Fat	7.8 grams
Saturated Fat	1.4 grams
Monounsat. Fat	1.9 grams
Polyunsat. Fat	3.1 grams
Cholesterol	73 mgs
Sodium	517 mgs

69

Quick Spanish Chicken with Rice

1 pound boneless, skinless chicken breasts
1 tablespoon vegetable oil
1/2 cup uncooked rice
1 onion, chopped
1 green pepper, chopped
1/2 teaspoon instant minced garlic
1 (8-ounce) can tomatoes
1 1/2 cups chicken broth
1/4 teaspoon chili powder
1/4 teaspoon pepper

Wash chicken and pat dry. Cut in thin slices 1/4-inch by 2 inches.

Heat oil in large skillet; add chicken and cook over medium-high heat until lightly browned.

Add rice, onion, green pepper, and garlic. Cook and stir about 3 minutes until onion begins to soften.

Add tomatoes, broth, chili powder, and pepper.

Cover, and simmer 15 minutes, or until rice is tender and liquid is absorbed, stirring once or twice. If more liquid is needed, add a small amount of water.

Makes 4 servings.

Tips...

Serve with broccoli, whole wheat toast, and fresh pineapple chunks or pineapple canned in its own juice.

Recipe freezes well.

Analysis: (Each serving)

Calories	304
Total Fat	7.9 grams
Saturated Fat	1.6 grams
Monounsat. Fat	2.3 grams
Polyunsat. Fat	3.1 grams
Cholesterol	73 mgs
Sodium	461 mgs

Chicken Chili

1 pound boneless,
   skinless chicken
   thighs
1/2 tablespoon
   vegetable oil
1 large onion, chopped
2 ribs celery, sliced
1 clove garlic, minced
1 (14-ounce) can
   tomatoes
1 (15-ounce) can red
   kidney beans,
   drained
1 green pepper, diced
2 teaspoons chili powder
   or to taste
3/4 teaspoon ground
   cumin seed
1/4 teaspoon salt
1/4 teaspoon
   black pepper

Wash chicken and pat dry. Remove visible fat. Cut chicken in 1/2-inch pieces.

In large non-stick skillet over medium-high heat, cook chicken in hot oil until meat is lightly browned.

Add onion, celery, and garlic; cook over medium heat until vegetables are tender.

Add tomatoes, stirring to break up. Add all remaining ingredients.

Cover and allow to simmer for 10 minutes.

Remove cover and simmer 15 minutes, or until part of the liquid evaporates and chili thickens.

Makes 6 servings.

Tips...

Serve over hot brown rice, with carrot and raisin salad.

Recipe freezes well.

Analysis: (Each serving)

Calories	220
Total Fat	7.3 grams
Saturated Fat	1.7 grams
Monounsat. Fat	2.4 grams
Polyunsat. Fat	2.3 grams
Cholesterol	45 mgs
Sodium	569 mgs

Ten-minute Springtime Chicken

1 pound boneless,
   skinless chicken
   breasts
1 tablespoon vegetable oil
1 medium onion, chopped
1/2 teaspoon instant
   minced garlic
1 (4-ounce) can
   mushrooms, drained
1 medium green pepper,
   cut in 3/4-inch pieces
1 (8-ounce) can tomatoes,
   cut-up or mashed
1/2 cup dry red wine
2 teaspoons parsley
   flakes
1/2 teaspoon oregano
   leaves
1/2 teaspoon basil leaves
1/2 teaspoon salt
1/4 teaspoon
   black pepper
1 tablespoon flour,
   optional

Wash and dry chicken and cut in 1-inch pieces.

Place oil in large skillet over high heat; add chicken pieces, stirring to coat with oil.

Cook until chicken changes color and is lightly browned, stirring occasionally.

Add onion and garlic to chicken; cook over moderate heat until onion is soft.

Add remaining ingredients. Bring to a boil over high heat, then simmer until vegetables are tender, about 5 minutes.

For thicker gravy, combine 1 tablespoon flour with two tablespoons water; add to chicken and cook 2 to 3 minutes longer.

Makes 4 servings.

Tips...

Serve with hot cooked brown rice and crisp raw carrot slices.

You may substitute broth (beef, chicken, or vegetable) for the wine.

Recipe freezes well.

Analysis: (Each serving)

Calories	234
Total Fat	7.0 grams
Saturated Fat	1.4 grams
Monounsat. Fat	1.9 grams
Polyunsat. Fat	2.9 grams
Cholesterol	73 mgs
Sodium	431 mgs

Sweet and Sour Chicken

1 tablespoon
vegetable oil
1 pound boneless,
skinless chicken
breasts, cut
in 3/4-inch pieces
1 tablespoon cornstarch
1 1/2 cups frozen mixed
vegetables (corn,
peas, green beans,
carrots)
1 (15-ounce) can chunk
pineapple in juice
1 tablespoon soy sauce
1 tablespoon reduced
sodium soy sauce
1/4 cup cider vinegar
1/4 cup brown sugar
2 tablespoons catsup
1/2 teaspoon instant
minced garlic
1/8 teaspoon black pepper

Heat oil in a large non-stick skillet or wok. Add chicken; stir and cook over high heat until lightly browned. Remove from heat.

Sprinkle cornstarch over chicken; stir to combine. Add remaining ingredients.

Cook and stir over high heat until mixture comes to a full boil. Cover; simmer over low heat until vegetables are tender, about 5 minutes.

Makes 5 servings.

Tips...

Serve over hot cooked rice; crisp raw celery on the side.

For a nice variation, use a large red or green pepper cut in 1/2-inch pieces instead of the frozen vegetables.

Recipe freezes well.

Analysis: (Each serving)

Calories	285
Total fat	5.3 grams
Saturated Fat	1.1 grams
Monounsat. Fat	1.5 grams
Polyunsat. Fat	2.2 grams
Cholesterol	58 mgs
Sodium	464 mgs

Tender Oven Cooked Chicken

4 chicken thighs
4 chicken drumsticks
1/2 cup cornflake crumbs
1/2 teaspoon paprika
1/2 teaspoon onion
    powder
1/2 teaspoon salt
1/4 teaspoon
    black pepper
1/8 teaspoon garlic
    powder
1/2 cup skim milk

Remove skin and visible fat from chicken pieces. Wash chicken and pat dry. Combine cornflake crumbs and seasonings. Dip chicken first in milk and then in crumb mixture to coat.

Place chicken pieces in shallow baking pan that has been sprayed with vegetable cooking spray. (For easier clean-up, line baking pan with aluminum foil.) Bake uncovered, in a preheated 350-degree oven 40 to 50 minutes until done.

❖ *Alternate MICROWAVE Cooking Instructions:*

Coat chicken with crumb mixture as above. Arrange chicken in microwave baking dish with thicker portions of thighs and breasts facing outside edges of dish. Place thinner pieces such as bony part of drumstick toward center. Cover lightly with wax paper. Cook on full power 10 to 14 minutes, or until chicken is done. Uncover, and let stand 5 minutes before serving.

Makes 4 servings.

Tips...

Corn on the cob and carrot and raisin salad go well with this chicken. Cook corn still in its husk in the microwave oven before you cook the chicken. The corn will stay hot if you do not remove the husk until just before serving.

The skin pulls easily from the chicken thighs. To remove skin easily from the drumstick, first cut the skin with a pair of kitchen shears.

Putting thicker parts of chicken toward corners or outside edges of baking dish promotes even cooking in the microwave oven.

Analysis: (Each serving)

Calories	249
Total Fat	8.3 grams
Saturated Fat	2.3 grams
Monounsat. Fat	3.0 grams
Polyunsat. Fat	1.9
Cholesterol	90 mgs
Sodium	505 mgs

Orange Sauced Chicken

4 chicken breast halves,
   boned and skinned
   (1 pound)
1/2 tablespoon
   vegetable oil
3 green onions, cut in
   1/4 inch pieces
1/2 cup unsweetened
   orange juice
1/2 teaspoon salt
1/4 teaspoon
   black pepper
1 1/2 teaspoons
   cornstarch
2 tablespoons water

Wash chicken breasts and pat dry.

In hot oil in nonstick skillet, cook chicken until lightly browned on both sides.

Add green onions, reserving the tops, orange juice, salt and pepper.

Cover and cook over low heat 10-15 minutes until chicken juices run clear when pricked with a fork.

Combine cornstarch and water; add to chicken and cook until sauce thickens.

Place chicken on warm platter; sprinkle reserved onion tops over all.

Makes 4 servings.

Tips...

Serve with hot cooked brown rice, zucchini with cherry tomatoes, and a fresh fruit salad.

Analysis: (Each serving)

Calories	174
Total Fat	4.8 grams
Saturated Fat	1.1 grams
Monounsat. Fat	1.5 grams
Polyunsat. Fat	1.7 grams
Cholesterol	73 mgs
Sodium	331 mgs

Chicken Breasts with White Wine

1 pound boneless, skinless chicken breasts
2 tablespoons flour
1/4 teaspoon salt
1/4 teaspoon pepper
1/2 tablespoon margarine
1/2 tablespoon olive oil
1/2 cup dry white wine
2 tablespoons chopped fresh parsley

Wash and dry chicken breasts. Pound chicken if necessary until the pieces are 1/2-inch thick or less.

Combine flour, salt and pepper. Roll chicken in flour and shake off excess.

Heat margarine and oil in a large non-stick skillet. Cook chicken in a single layer over medium heat until lightly browned. Remove from skillet and reserve.

Add wine to skillet. Cook over high heat, scraping particles from bottom of skillet, until wine boils and cooks about 30 seconds.

Return chicken to skillet. Cover and simmer over low heat 10 minutes or until chicken is done.

Add parsley. Place chicken on serving platter; pour pan juices over.

Makes 4 servings.

Tips...

Serve with new potatoes and peas, and a fruit salad of diced fresh fruit moistened with orange juice.

Alcohol evaporates leaving only a nice flavor. If you prefer, omit the alcohol, cook chicken until done and then squeeze a tablespoon or two of fresh lemon juice over the chicken.

Analysis: (Each serving)

Calories	209
Total Fat	6.2 grams
Saturated Fat	1.3 grams
Monounsat. Fat	3.0 grams
Polyunsat. Fat	1.3 grams
Cholesterol	73 mgs
Sodium	212 mgs

Chicken and Asparagus Parmesan

1 pound fresh asparagus, or 1 (10-ounce) package frozen spears

Cook fresh asparagus as directed in vegetable section, or cook frozen asparagus according to package directions. Drain, but do not season. Place in shallow baking dish.

4 chicken breast halves, boned and skinned
1/4 teaspoon salt
1/4 teaspoon black pepper

Wash and dry chicken breasts. Pound meat to make it no thicker than 1/2-inch.

Season chicken breasts with salt and pepper. Coat pieces, using 2 tablespoons flour; shake to remove excess flour . Place margarine and oil in non-stick skillet over medium heat; add chicken in single layer and cook until lightly browned and done. Arrange chicken on top of asparagus.

1/4 cup flour, divided
1/2 tablespoon margarine
1/2 tablespoon olive oil
1/3 cup white wine
2/3 cup chicken broth
1/4 cup grated Parmesan cheese

Combine remaining 2 tablespoons flour with wine and chicken broth; stir briskly and add to skillet. Boil until sauce thickens and cook about 1 minute more. Pour over chicken. Sprinkle Parmesan cheese over all. Bake uncovered in 350-degree oven 20 minutes or until heated through.

Makes 4 servings.

Tips...

Use leftover cooked turkey or chicken slices and omit the steps of cooking the chicken breasts. Prepare the gravy in a saucepan.

Recipe may be prepared ahead and heated in oven just before serving, a nice dish for company.

Serve with new potatoes and fruit salad of assorted fresh fruits in season. Add orange juice to keep fruit from turning brown.

Analysis: (Each serving)

Calories	268
Total Fat	8.9 grams
Saturated Fat	2.7 grams
Monounsat. Fat	3.6 grams
Polyunsat. Fat	1.6 grams
Cholesterol	78 mgs
Sodium	461 mgs

Deviled Chicken

1 pound boneless,
   skinless chicken
   breasts
1 tablespoon margarine,
   melted
1 1/2 teaspoons
   paprika
1/2 teaspoon
   dry mustard
1/2 teaspoon salt
1/4 to 1/2 teaspoon
   chili powder

Wash and dry chicken breasts; cut each breast half into 3 pieces. Place chicken pieces in lightly oiled shallow pan, or spray pan with vegetable coating spray.

Combine margarine with remaining ingredients and spread evenly on chicken pieces.

Cover; bake at 350-degrees about 30 minutes or until chicken is done.

Place chicken on warm serving platter, pour pan juices over.

Tips...

Serve with easy scalloped potatoes, green beans and combination salad.

Analysis: (Each serving)

Calories	172
Total Fat	6.0 grams
Saturated Fat	1.4 grams
Monounsat. Fat	2.4 grams
Polyunsat. Fat	1.8 grams
Cholesterol	73 mgs
Sodium	382 mgs

Skillet Lasagna

1 pound ground turkey
1 1/2 cups cottage cheese
(1 percent fat)
3 cups medium egg
noodles, uncooked
2 (14-ounce) cans cut-up
tomatoes
2 tablespoons instant
chopped onion
1 tablespoon
dried parsley
2 teaspoons dried basil
1 teaspoon sugar
1/4 teaspoon
black pepper
1/4 teaspoon instant
minced garlic

1 cup (4-ounces)
shredded part-skim
mozzarella cheese

Cook ground turkey over medium heat in a large non-stick skillet, or in a skillet coated with vegetable cooking spray, until the meat changes color. Remove from heat. Drain fat, if any.

Spread cottage cheese on top of ground turkey in skillet. Cover with uncooked noodles.

Combine the cut-up tomatoes with all remaining ingredients except the mozzarella cheese. Pour tomato mixture evenly over the noodles, moistening the noodles.

Cover. Cook over medium-high heat until mixture comes to a boil, then simmer over low heat 25 to 30 minutes, or until noodles are tender. After the first 10 minutes of cooking, check to be sure all noodles are moistened. If casserole seems too juicy, remove cover the last 5 minutes of cooking time.

Turn off heat. Sprinkle mozzarella over top of lasagna, cover, and let sit a few minutes until cheese melts. Cut into 8 wedges. Makes 8 servings.

Tips...

Serve with green peas, a combination salad that does not include tomatoes, and crusty bread.

Leftover casserole may be stored, covered, in refrigerator for several days, or may be frozen.

Cook ground turkey with care; overcooking makes it dry and tough.

Analysis: (Each serving)

Calories	305
Total Fat	6.4 grams
Saturated Fat	2.9 grams
Monounsat. Fat	1.7 grams
Polyunsat. Fat	1.1 grams
Cholesterol	75 mgs
Sodium	436 mgs

Turkey-Mac

1 pound ground turkey **1 large onion, chopped** **1 carrot, diced** **1 clove garlic, minced** **1 green pepper, diced** **1 (15-ounce) can** **tomato sauce** **1 (15-ounce) can water** **1 cup elbow macaroni,** **uncooked** **1 teaspoon oregano** **leaves, crushed** **1/8 teaspoon salt** **1/4 teaspoon** **black pepper**	In large non-stick skillet or heavy duty saucepan, cook turkey, onion, carrot, and garlic over medium heat until turkey changes color and vegetables start to soften. Drain fat. Stir in remaining ingredients; cover. Simmer over low heat 15 to 20 minutes until macaroni is tender, and liquid is absorbed. Stir several times while cooking. Makes 6 servings, 1 cup per serving.

Tips...

Sprinkle a teaspoon or two of Parmesan cheese over each serving, if desired.

Serve with fresh asparagus or green beans, baked apple slices and whole wheat toast.

Leftovers may be frozen.

Analysis: (Each serving)

Calories	206
Total Fat	2.9 grams
Saturated Fat	1.0 grams
Monounsat. Fat	0.7 grams
Polyunsat. Fat	1.1 grams
Cholesterol	43 mgs
Sodium	553 mgs

FISH

When selecting fresh fish, look for a mild, non-fishy odor. Fillets and steaks should have a moist, freshly cut appearance. Whole fish should have bright, clear eyes, red or pink gills, and firmly attached scales. The flesh springs back lightly when touched.

Frozen fish is a good alternative if fresh fish is not available. Some packages have individually wrapped fillets, making them a good choice for small families. To dry fish that has been thawed, pat *lightly* with a paper towel; pressing too hard will remove moisture from the fish.

The most common mistake made with fish is overcooking. Fish is done when the flesh becomes opaque and flakes easily with a fork. Overcooking will toughen and dry out the flesh.

Broiled Fish Steaks

1 pound fish steaks,
  such as salmon,
  halibut, tuna
  or snapper
1 tablespoon melted
  margarine
1 tablespoon
  lemon juice
Season with your choice
  of parsley, thyme,
  dill, marjoram,
  basil, savory.
  Or, sprinkle with
  Cajun type seasoning

Lemon wedges

Wash fish and pat lightly with paper towel to dry.

Place fish in greased baking dish.

Combine margarine and lemon juice to make basting sauce; brush on fish and sprinkle with seasoning of your choice.

Place fish 4 or 5 inches from the source of heat in a preheated broiler. Cook fish ten minutes per inch of thickness. Turn fish over halfway through cooking time, baste and season top side.

Fish is done when it begins to flake when tested with a fork but is still moist.

Transfer fish to warm serving platter. Serve with lemon wedges.

Makes 4 servings.

Tips...

Serve with baked potatoes, summer squash, and cole slaw.

Prick potatoes with a fork and bake in the microwave oven. Remove potatoes from oven when they are still a little firm. Wrap in a clean towel. Potatoes will continue to cook outside the oven and will keep hot while you prepare the squash in the microwave oven. For more moist potatoes, wrap in aluminum foil after you remove them from the oven.

Analysis: (Each serving, using salmon)

Calories	201
Total Fat	9.0 grams
Saturated Fat	2.0 grams
Monounsat. Fat	4.3 grams
Polyunsat. Fat	2.8 grams
Cholesterol	75 mgs
Sodium	94 mgs

Baked Herbed Fish

1 pound fish fillets, such as cod, flounder or trout
1 1/2 tablespoons margarine, melted
1 1/2 tablespoons lemon juice
1 teaspoon parsley flakes
1/2 teaspoon basil leaves
1/2 teaspoon paprika
1/4 teaspoon salt
1/8 teaspoon garlic powder

Place fish in a greased baking pan.

Combine remaining ingredients and spoon evenly over fish.

Bake in preheated 350-degree oven 10 to 15 minutes until fish is opaque and flakes easily with a fork; do not overcook.

Makes 4 servings.

❖ *Alternate MICROWAVE cooking instructions:*

Place fish in a shallow microwave baking dish and prepare as above. Cover with wax paper.
Cook in microwave oven on full power about 4 minutes or until fish flakes easily with a fork.

Tips...

Serve with easy scalloped potatoes, green peas, and a combination salad.

Use other seasonings on fish as desired: oregano, dill, ground red pepper, onion powder.

Analysis: (Each serving, using cod.)

Calories	158
Total Fat	5.3 grams
Saturated Fat	0.9 grams
Monounsat. Fat	2.0 grams
Polyunsat. Fat	2.0 grams
Cholesterol	61 mgs
Sodium	264 mgs

Tomato-Cheese Fillets

1 tablespoon margarine
2 tablespoons finely
**   chopped onion**
1 pound fish fillets
**   such as**
**   cod, flounder, trout**
1/4 teaspoon salt
1/8 teaspoon black pepper
1 large tomato, diced
3 tablespoons grated
**   Parmesan cheese**
Paprika, optional

Place margarine and onion in a 1-cup glass measure and cook on full power 1 1/2 minutes or until onion is soft.

Arrange fish in a shallow baking dish with thicker edges of fish to outside of dish. Sprinkle salt and pepper over fish; cover with diced tomato pieces.

Spread margarine and onions evenly over tomatoes.

Cover with wax paper; cook 3 minutes on full power.

Sprinkle with Parmesan cheese. Cover with waxed paper; cook 1 minute more or until fish flakes easily when tested with a fork.

Sprinkle with paprika.

Makes 4 servings.

Tips...

Serve with sliced potatoes with onion, a green vegetable, and cole slaw.

Cook the potatoes in the microwave oven. Let them stand while cooking the fish. If necessary, reheat potatoes just before serving.

Analysis: (Each serving, using cod)

Calories	169
Total Fat	5.4 grams
Saturated Fat	1.5 grams
Monounsat. Fat	1.7 grams
Polyunsat. Fat	1.5 grams
Cholesterol	64 grams
Sodium	324 mgs

Stir-Fry Orange Roughy

1 1/4 pounds orange
   roughy
2 tablespoons cornstarch
3 1/2 tablespoons
   vegetable oil
2 green onions, chopped
2 carrots, diced small
2 ribs celery, diced

Seasoning Sauce:
  1 tablespoon soy sauce
  1 teaspoon cornstarch
  1 tablespoon white
   wine or dry sherry
  1/2 cup chicken broth

2 1/2 cups hot cooked
  rice (3/4 cup
  uncooked)

Cut each orange roughy fillet into four pieces. Coat with 1 tablespoon oil.

Sprinkle cornstarch over fish. Roll fish over several times until cornstarch dissolves. Let stand 20 to 30 minutes while preparing vegetables and seasoning sauce.

Heat 2 tablespoons oil in wok or skillet. Cook fish four pieces at a time.

Remove to a hot platter. When all fish is done, add remaining 1/2 tablespoon oil and stir fry carrots for 1 minute. Add several tablespoons of water if more moisture is needed. Add onion and celery; continue to stir fry for several minutes. Put fish back in pan.

Pour seasoning sauce over fish and vegetables. Place rice on a heated platter. As soon as sauce thickens, serve the fish over the rice.

Makes 5 servings.

Tips...

Orange roughy comes from New Zealand, each fillet frozen separately. Three fillets make about 1 1/4 pounds.

Serve with broccoli or spinach, baked or sliced tomatoes and crusty bread.

Adapted from a Landlock/Booth recipe.

Analysis: (Each serving, includes 1/2 cup rice)

Calories	372
Total Fat	12.5 grams
Saturated Fat	1.6 grams
Monounsat. Fat	3.4 grams
Polyunsat. Fat	6.5 grams
Cholesterol	59 mgs
Sodium	416 mgs

Rosey Fish Stew

1 (14-ounce) can
  cut-up tomatoes
1/2 cup dry white wine
1/4 cup chopped
  fresh parsley
1 teaspoon basil leaves
1 1/4 cups chicken broth
1/8 teaspoon sugar
1/8 teaspoon pepper
1 pound fillets of white
  fish, cut in 2-inch
  pieces

In saucepan, simmer tomatoes, wine, parsley, and basil about 2 minutes.

Add remaining ingredients. Simmer 10 minutes or until done, stirring often.

Makes 4 servings.

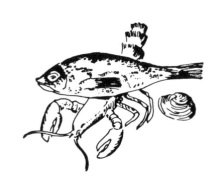

Tips...

Serve stew in a bowl.

Serve with corn-on-the-cob, carrot and celery sticks and crusty bread.

Before adding basil, crush the leaves between your fingers to release more flavor.

Analysis: (Each serving, using flounder or sole)

Calories	159
Total Fat	2.2 grams
Saturated Fat	0.5 grams
Monounsat. Fat	0.5 grams
Polyunsat. Fat	0.7 grams
Cholesterol	70 mgs
Sodium	544 mgs

Stir-Fry Shrimp with Snow Peas

1 pound raw shrimp in
   shells, approx. 30
   to the pound
1 tablespoon vegetable oil
1 slice gingerroot
   1/8-inch thick,
   about the size
   of a quarter
1 clove garlic, peeled
3/4 pound fresh snow
   peas

Seasoning Sauce:
   4 tablespoons water
   2 1/3 tablespoons soy
     sauce
   2 tablespoons dry
     sherry
   1 tablespoon
     cornstarch

Combine seasoning sauce ingredients; reserve.

Shell and devein shrimp. Wash shrimp and pat dry with a paper towel. Heat oil in nonstick skillet or wok over medium-high heat. Add garlic and gingerroot; cook 10 seconds, then add shrimp.

Stir and cook 2 minutes, or until shrimp turn pink. Remove shrimp to warm platter. Discard garlic and gingerroot.

Over medium heat, add snowpeas to wok or skillet. If wok or skillet is dry, add several tablespoons of water with the snow peas. Stir and cook about 2 minutes; snowpeas should be hot and crispy tender.

Add cooked shrimp to snowpeas; pour seasoning sauce over all. Cook and stir long enough for sauce to boil and thicken.

Makes 4 servings.

Tips...

Serve over hot cooked rice. Serve with carrot and raisin salad or sliced tomatoes.

Analysis: (Each serving)

Calories	172
Total Fat	4.4 grams
Saturated Fat	0.6 grams
Monounsat. Fat	1.0 grams
Polyunsat. Fat	2.5 grams
Cholesterol	107 mgs
Sodium	573 mgs

Shrimp Creole

2 medium onions,
    chopped
2 celery ribs, diced
1 green pepper, diced
1 tablespoon
    vegetable oil
1 tablespoon flour
1 (14 1/2-ounce) can
    tomatoes
1/4 cup water
1 tablespoon catsup
1 teaspoon chili powder
1/2 teaspoon salt

1 1/3 cups cooked shrimp
    (1 pound raw shrimp
    in shells)

Place onions, celery, and green pepper in a 2-quart casserole; add the oil, stirring to coat vegetables.

Cook, covered, on full power 8 to 10 minutes or until vegetables are soft. Stir several times while cooking.

Stir in flour; add remaining ingredients except shrimp.

Cook, uncovered, on full power about 10 minutes, or until slightly thickened. Stir several times while cooking.

Add cooked shrimp; cook 1-2 minutes until heated through.

Makes 4 servings.

Tips...

Serve over hot cooked rice, with green beans and carrot sticks.

If frozen shrimp are used, thaw before cooking. To cook shrimp in microwave oven, arrange a single layer of shrimp in a shallow baking dish. Cover lightly with plastic wrap. Cook on full power 2 or 3 minutes per pound; stir halfway through cooking time. Let stand a few minutes to finish cooking.

Analysis: (Each serving)

Calories	200
Total Fat	5.2 grams
Saturated Fat	0.7 grams
Monounsat. Fat	1.1 grams
Polyunsat. Fat	2.7 grams
Cholesterol	128 mgs
Sodium	560 mgs

Spaghetti with Tuna Sauce

1 tablespoon olive oil
1 clove garlic, minced
1 (14-ounce) can
   Italian pear
   shaped tomatoes,
   mashed
2 tablespoons
   finely chopped
   fresh parsley
1/2 teaspoon
   oregano leaves
1/2 teaspoon
   basil leaves
1/8 teaspoon
   black pepper
1 (6-ounce) can tuna,
   well drained

3 cups hot cooked
   spaghetti
   (6 ounces uncooked)

In a 2-quart saucepan, combine all ingredients except tuna and spaghetti.

Cook, uncovered, 25 to 30 minutes until sauce thickens.

Add tuna and cook 3 or 4 minutes longer, until heated through.

Meanwhile, cook spaghetti according to directions on package.

Place spaghetti on warm platter; pour tuna sauce over.

Makes 3 servings.

Tips...

Serve with cauliflower and combination salad without tomatoes.

Analysis: (Each serving)

Calories	332
Total Fat	6.8 grams
Saturated Fat	0.9 grams
Monounsat. Fat	3.7 grams
Polyunsat. Fat	1.0 grams
Cholesterol	24 mgs
Sodium	464 mgs

Tuna Tetrazzini

2 cups egg noodles, uncooked

Cook egg noodles according to package directions. Reserve.

2 tablespoons flour
3/4 cup chicken broth, low sodium
3/4 cup canned evaporated skim milk

Meanwhile, in a 1 1/2-quart microwave casserole dish, stir flour into a small amount of the broth.

1 small clove garlic, minced, or
1/8 teaspoon garlic powder

Add remaining broth, milk, garlic, and pepper, blending well.

1/8 teaspoon black pepper
1 (6 1/2-ounce) can tuna packed in water, drained

Cook on full power in microwave oven, uncovered, 5 minutes or until mixture boils and thickens. Stir several times while cooking.

1 (4-ounce) can sliced mushrooms, drained
1/4 cup grated Parmesan cheese

Add noodles, tuna, mushrooms, and cheese to the thickened mixture. Cover, and cook on full power 5 minutes or until heated through. Stir one time while cooking.

1/8 teaspoon paprika

Sprinkle with paprika before serving.

Makes 3 servings.

Tips...

Serve with cooked carrots, pickled beets, and whole wheat toast.

One serving provides thirty percent of an adult's daily calcium requirement.

Analysis: (Each serving)

Calories	324
Total Fat	5.6 grams
Saturated Fat	2.1 grams
Monounsat. Fat	1.4 grams
Polyunsat. Fat	0.8 grams
Cholesterol	65 mgs
Sodium	569 mgs

Salmon Patties

1 (7 1/2-ounce) can pink salmon, drained, reserve liquid
1/2 cup fine dry bread crumbs
2 egg whites
2 tablespoons finely chopped onion
2 tablespoons chopped parsley
1 tablespoon lemon juice
1/4 teaspoon black pepper
1 tablespoon vegetable oil

Lemon wedges, optional

Place salmon in a bowl and mash bones with a fork.

Combine all ingredients, except the oil. Add 2 or 3 tablespoons reserved liquid from the salmon for moisture if needed.

Mix well; shape into patties.

Fry patties in oil over medium heat until lightly browned on both sides.

Serve with lemon wedges.

Makes 3 servings.

Tips...

The salmon bones provide calcium and are not noticeable when mashed.

To substitute dried instant minced onion and dried parsley leaves for fresh, use 2 teaspoons instant minced onion and 2 teaspoons dried parsley.

Serve with waffle potatoes or baked acorn squash, southern okra, a green salad and whole wheat toast.

Analysis: (Each serving)

Calories	221
Total fat	9.7 grams
Saturated	1.6 gram
Monounsat. Fat	2.7 grams
Polyunsat. Fat	4.7 grams
Cholesterol	29 mgs
Sodium	526 mgs

Spaghetti with Red Clam Sauce

1 (10-ounce) can baby
   clams
1 (14-ounce) can Italian
   pear-shaped
   tomatoes, cut up
1/3 to 1/2 cup juice
   from clams
1/3 cup chopped fresh
   parsley
1 1/2 tablespoons
   olive oil
2 cloves garlic, minced
1/2 teaspoon dried basil
1/2 teaspoon
   oregano leaves
1/4 teaspoon salt
1/4 teaspoon
   black pepper

4 cups hot cooked
   spaghetti (8 ounces
   uncooked)

Drain clams; reserve juice. If juice is sandy, strain. If clams are sandy, rinse with water after reserving clam juice.

In a 2-quart saucepan, combine tomatoes, clam juice, parsley, olive oil, garlic, basil, oregano, salt and black pepper. Bring to a boil; simmer, uncovered 25 to 30 minutes until sauce thickens.

Add clams; heat gently 3 to 5 minutes.

Meanwhile cook spaghetti according to package directions. Drain. Place on warm platter, pour sauce over and serve immediately.

Makes 4 servings.

Tips...

Liguini, which is a little thicker than spaghetti, is often used for this dish.

Serve with a green vegetable, toasted French bread, and a combination salad without tomatoes.

Analysis: (Each serving)

Calories	318
Total Fat	8.0 grams
Saturated Fat	1.2 grams
Monounsat. Fat	4.3 grams
Polyunsat. Fat	1.1 grams
Cholesterol	34 mgs
Sodium	372 mgs

DRY BEANS & GRAINS

Dry beans and grains are foods that are high in complex carbohydrates.

Recipes in this section have the least amount of fat needed to maintain good taste. Extra spices and herbs are added when the amount of fat is decreased.

Several of the recipes are meatless main dishes.

Because of the long cooking time required for dry beans it's a good idea to prepare extras to freeze for later use. Recipes included here each call for one pound of dry beans. But if you can't use that many or haven't the freezer space, recipe may be halved.

Stuffed Shells Florentine

❖ MICROWAVE/CONVENTIONAL

15 jumbo shell macaroni, cooked firm, drained and cooled

Tomato Sauce:
1 cup chopped onion
1/4 cup water
1 (15-ounce) can no-salt-added tomato sauce
1 teaspoon sugar
1/2 teaspoon basil leaves
1/2 teaspoon oregano leaves
1/4 teaspoon instant minced garlic
1/8 teaspoon salt
1/8 teaspoon pepper

Cheese Stuffing:
1 cup part-skim ricotta cheese
1 cup (4 ounces) shredded part-skim mozzarella cheese
1/4 cup grated Parmesan cheese
1 egg white, slightly beaten
1 (10-ounce) package frozen chopped spinach, cooked and very well drained
1/2 teaspoon oregano leaves
1/8 teaspoon salt

To make sauce in the microwave oven, combine onion and water in a 1 1/2-quart covered casserole. Cook on full power until onion is soft, about 5 minutes. Stir one time while cooking. Add remaining sauce ingredients and cook, uncovered, 5 minutes longer. Makes about 2 1/4 cups.

Combine stuffing ingredients, mixing well. Stuff 2 to 3 tablespoons cheese mixture into each shell. In 12" x 8" baking dish, spread a layer of 1/3 of the tomato sauce. Arrange shells, stuffed side up, in sauce. Spoon remaining sauce over shells.

Cover with aluminum foil. Bake in conventional oven at 350 degrees for 30 minutes, or until hot. Makes 5 servings.

Tips...

Serve with fresh cooked broccoli, a combination salad without tomatoes and crusty bread.

Recipe freezes well.

A serving provides over forty-five percent of an adult's daily calcium requirement.

Analysis: (Each serving of 3 stuffed shells)

Calories	308
Total Fat	10.0 grams
Saturated Fat	5.9 grams
Monounsat. Fat	2.7 grams
Polyunsat. Fat	0.5 grams
Cholesterol	31 mgs
Sodium	495 mgs

Pasta with Creamy Walnut Sauce

1 tablespoon olive oil
1/2 cup walnuts
1/4 cup part-skim
    ricotta cheese
1/2 cup evaporated
    skim milk
1/4 cup plus 2
    tablespoons grated
    Parmesan cheese
2 tablespoons
    chopped parsley
1/4 teaspoon salt
1/4 teaspoon black pepper

8 cups hot cooked
    fettuccini or linguini
    (1 pound uncooked)
1 1/2 tablespoons
    margarine, melted

Place oil, walnuts, ricotta and 1/4 cup milk in blender or in food processor bowl. Process until nuts are finely chopped.

Add remaining milk, 1/4 cup Parmesan cheese, parsley, salt, and pepper, blending well. Reserve.

Cook pasta according to package directions. Drain, and toss with melted margarine.

For each serving, place 1 1/3 cups pasta on plate, top with 2 1/2 tablespoons sauce and sprinkle with 1 teaspoon Parmesan.

Makes 6 servings.

Tips...

Serve with a green vegetable, combination salad, and crusty bread.

If sauce is too thick, add additional skim milk; if too thin, add Parmesan cheese.

Sauce keeps several days in refrigerator. Bring to room temperature before serving.

Analysis: (Each serving)

Calories	420
Total Fat	15.5 grams
Saturated Fat	3.0 grams
Monounsat. Fat	5.2 grams
Polyunsat. Fat	5.5 grams
Cholesterol	8 mgs
Sodium	247 mgs

Quick Macaroni and Cheese

1 cup elbow macaroni,
  uncooked
2 tablespoons flour
1/2 teaspoon dry mustard
1/8 teaspoon black
  pepper
1 cup skim milk
1 tablespoon finely
  chopped onion or 2
  teaspoons instant
  minced onion
1 cup (4-ounces)
  shredded process
  American cheese
  (or cut in thin strips)

Cook macaroni according to package directions. Drain. Place macaroni in a 2-quart saucepan.

Mix flour, mustard, and pepper with 1/2 cup milk until smooth. Mix with remaining milk, onion, and cheese. Stir into macaroni.

Cook over low heat, stirring constantly until sauce thickens, about 10 minutes.

If desired, sprinkle with paprika before serving.

Makes 4 servings, 2/3 cup each.

❖ *Alternate MICROWAVE cooking instructions:*

Place cooked macaroni in a microwave-safe casserole. Mix flour, mustard, and pepper with 1/2 cup milk until smooth. Mix with remaining milk and onion. Stir into cooked macaroni. Cook, uncovered, stirring every minute, for 3 minutes or until sauce thickens. Stir in cheese. If needed, cook 30 seconds longer until cheese melts.

Tips...

Serve with zucchini with cherry tomatoes, carrot sticks, raw apple slices, and whole wheat toast.

Close to forty percent of the calories in this recipe come from fat. When you balance it with the low-fat accompaniments, your meal comes to under thirty percent fat.

Each serving provides over one-fourth of an adult's daily calcium requirement.

Analysis: (Each 2/3 cup serving)

Calories	238
Total Fat	9.7 grams
Saturated Fat	5.7 grams
Monounsat. Fat	2.6 grams
Polyunsat. Fat	0.5 grams
Cholesterol	28 mgs
Sodium	454 mgs

Ranch Style Beans

1 package (1 pound) pinto beans **7 cups cold water** **1 large onion, diced** **1 tablespoon vegetable oil** **2 cloves garlic** **2 teaspoons chili powder or to taste** **2 teaspoons salt** **1 (15-ounce) can tomatoes**	Rinse beans well and remove any debris that may be present. Cover beans with 7 cups of water and let stand 6 to 8 hours or overnight. Or, use two-minute boil soaking/cooking method: Combine 7 cups water and beans. Bring to vigorous boil; boil 2 minutes. Remove from heat; cover and let stand 1-2 hours. Bring beans and soaking water to a boil. Add oil, onion, garlic, chili powder and salt.

Cover, and simmer 1 1/2 hours. Stir occasionally while cooking.

Add the tomatoes and cook 1 hour longer or until beans are tender. If necessary, add enough water to keep beans covered.

Makes 8 cups, or 12 (2/3-cup) servings.

Tips...

Adding oil reduces amount of foam that forms while beans cook. Adding the tomatoes too soon delays softening of beans.

Do not add baking soda to beans; too much soda will affect the flavor of beans and their nutritional value.

Serve over hot cooked white or brown rice along with a fresh fruit salad.

Add a small amount of meat if you desire.

Cooked beans freeze well.

Analysis: (Each 2/3 cup serving)

Calories	174
Total fat	1.9 grams
Saturated Fat	0.3 grams
Monounsat. Fat	0.4 grams
Polyunsat. Fat	1.1 grams
Sodium	421 mgs

Creole Beans

1 (1 pound) package small white beans
7 cups cold water
1 large onion, chopped
1 tablespoon oil
1 teaspoon salt
1 (15 ounce) can cut-up tomatoes
1 green pepper, diced
Dash cayenne pepper, or few drops hot pepper sauce, optional

Rinse and sort beans.

Cover with water and let stand 6 to 8 hours or overnight.

Or, use the two-minute boil/soaking cooking method:
Combine 7 cups water and beans. Bring to vigorous boil; boil 2 minutes.
Remove from heat, cover and let stand 1 to 2 hours.

Add onion, oil, salt, and, if needed, a small amount of additional water to cover beans. Simmer, covered, 1 1/2 hours. Stir occasionally while cooking.

Add remaining ingredients and cook an hour longer, or until beans are tender.

Makes 8 cups, 16 servings of 1/2 cup each.

Tips...

Serve with a small sandwich. Have tuna, lean roast, ham or chicken on whole wheat bread with lettuce and tomato.

Cooked beans keep up to 5 days in refrigerator.

Freeze extras in meal size portions in plastic freezer bags.

Analysis: (Each 1/2 cup serving)

Calories	120
Total Fat	1.5 grams
Saturated Fat	0.2 grams
Monounsat. Fat	0.3 grams
Polyunsat. Fat	0.9 grams
Cholesterol	0 mgs
Sodium	182 mgs

Lentils

1 package (1 pound) dry
    lentils
7 cups water
1 large onion, chopped
1 carrot, diced
1 rib celery with leaves,
    diced
1 clove garlic, minced
1 tablespoon oil
1 1/2 teaspoons salt
1/2 teaspoon pepper
1 bay leaf
1/8 teaspoon thyme

Rinse and sort lentils. Combine all ingredients.

Bring to a boil. Cover and simmer gently 2 hours, or until lentils are mealy tender. Add more water as needed.

Remove bay leaf before serving.

Makes 8 cups, 16 servings of 1/2 cup each.

Tips...

Cooked lentils keep several days in the refrigerator, or may be frozen.

They go well with sandwiches or with any plain meat.

Dry beans and peas, including lentils, contain insoluble fiber that may help lower cholesterol levels.

Analysis: (Each serving)

Calories	121
Total Fat	1.4 grams
Saturated Fat	0.2 grams
Monounsat. Fat	0.3 grams
Polyunsat. Fat	0.8 grams
Cholesterol	0.0 mgs
Sodium	217 mgs

Baked Rice

1 cup parboiled rice
2 1/2 cups chicken broth,
    approximately
1 small onion, chopped
1 tablespoon margarine

Preheat oven to 400-degrees.

Stir together all ingredients in a 2-quart ovenproof casserole, adding chicken broth instead of water in the amount listed on rice package directions.

Cover and bake 35 minutes, or until done.

Fluff with a fork just before serving.

Makes 7 servings, approximately 1/2 cup each.

Tips...

To shorten cooking time to 25 minutes, heat the broth to boiling before adding to rice.

Rice may be baked at 350-degrees for approximately 45 minutes.

Use canned broth, or bouillon cubes or granules.

Parboiled or converted rice is processed in a special way to retain more nutrients than other white rice. Any white rice may be used in this recipe except "instant." Instant rice retains fewer nutrients than other rice.

Analysis: (Each serving)

Calories	126
Total Fat	2.5 grams
Saturated Fat	0.5 grams
Monounsat. Fat	1.0 grams
Polyunsat. Fat	0.8 grams
Cholesterol	0.0 mgs
Sodium	298 mgs

SALADS & VEGETABLES

Plain cooked vegetables can taste excellent, but most of us like a little seasoning added. Recipes included here are seasoned with spices, herbs, and lemon juice with only a minimum amount of fat added. Some vegetables are seasoned with a small amount of olive oil, but you may substitute margarine if you prefer.

Cooking vegetables as quickly as possible in only a small amount of water preserves nutrients, flavor and color. One of the best ways to do this is by cooking them in a microwave oven. For this reason many of the recipes in this section specify cooking in a microwave oven. As an alternative, steam vegetables over boiling water on a traditional range.

Carrot and Raisin Salad

3 cups grated carrots,
about 3/4 pound as
purchased
1 (8-ounce) can crushed
pineapple in juice,
drain lightly,
reserve juice
1/4 cup raisins
2 tablespoons reduced
calorie mayonnaise
or salad dressing
2 tablespoons reserved
pineapple juice
1 teaspoon sugar
1/8 teaspoon salt

Place carrots, pineapple, and raisins in a medium bowl.

Combine remaining ingredients; pour over carrot mixture and stir well.

Chill before serving.

Makes 7 servings of 1/2 cup each.

Tips...

You may want to adjust the sugar depending on the sweetness of the carrots.

This salad goes well with ham, or with some of the Chinese type stir-fry dishes.

Analysis (Each serving)

Calories	68
Total Fat	0.9 grams
Saturated Fat	0.2 grams
Monounsat. Fat	0.2 grams
Polyunsat. Fat	0.5 grams
Cholesterol	1.0 mgs
Sodium	77 mgs

Cole Slaw

**1 1/4 pound cabbage,
coarsely grated
(6 to 8 cups)
2 carrots, grated
1/2 onion, chopped fine**

**Dressing:
3 tablespoons oil
3 tablespoons vinegar
3 tablespoons sugar
1/2 teaspoon salt
1/4 teaspoon
celery seed
1/3 teaspoon dry
mustard, or
1 teaspoon
prepared mustard**

Place cabbage, carrots and onion in large bowl.

Combine dressing ingredients and bring to a boil. Pour over cabbage mixture, tossing to coat. Cover slaw and refrigerate 4 hours, or overnight. Toss again before serving.

Keeps up to 4 days in refrigerator.

Makes 12 servings.

Tips...

When preparing the dressing, it may seem like a small amount. After pouring it over the slaw, stir well and it will coat the cabbage mixture.

Analysis: (Each serving)

Calories	60
Total Fat	3.6 grams
Saturated Fat	0.4 grams
Monounsat. Fat	0.9 grams
Polyunsat. Fat	2.1 grams
Cholesterol	0 mgs
Sodium	107 mgs

Pasta Salad with Shrimp

1 pound package linguine
1/4 cup plus 1 tablespoon
    olive oil, divided
1 tablespoon margarine
1 pound cleaned shrimp
1 garlic clove, minced
3 tablespoons
    lemon juice
Dash cayenne pepper
1 red or green pepper,
    cut in 1-inch
    matchstick pieces
1 red onion, thinly sliced
12 small black
    olives, chopped
1/2 cup chopped parsley
1 tablespoon chopped
    fresh basil, or
    1 teaspoon dried
1 teaspoon salt
1/2 teaspoon
    black pepper
3 tomatoes, cut in
    wedges

Cook linguine according to package directions. Drain, rinse with cold water and drain again.

In a large bowl, toss linguine with 1/4 cup olive oil, coating well. Reserve.

Wash shrimp and pat dry. In a large nonstick skillet, heat the 1 tablespoon margarine with remaining tablespoon of olive oil.

Add shrimp and garlic; cook, stirring often, 5 minutes or until shrimp are pink and tender. Remove from heat. Add cayenne and lemon juice to shrimp; marinate about 30 minutes.

Combine remaining ingredients, except tomatoes, with linguine. Add shrimp mixture. Toss well. Chill; toss again just before serving. Garnish with tomato wedges.

Makes 10 servings, about 1 cup each.

Tips...

Serve with baked tomatoes and crusty bread.

To avoid mushy pasta, select dry pasta products made with 100% durum wheat or semolina flour.

Analysis: (Each serving)

Calories	302
Total Fat	10.3 grams
Saturated Fat	1.4 grams
Monounsat. Fat	6.3 grams
Polyunsat. Fat	1.6 grams
Cholesterol	68 mgs
Sodium	287 mgs

Pasta Salad Parmesan

2 cups vegetable-flavored
   macaroni twists,
   uncooked
1 1/2 cups broccoli
   flowerets
1/2 cup chopped
   green pepper
1/2 cup chopped celery
1/4 cup chopped parsley
1 1/2 cups cherry tomato
   halves
1 cup diced cooked
   chicken breast

Herb Dressing:
1/4 cup olive oil
3 tablespoons wine vinegar
1 tablespoon lemon juice
1 tablespoon chopped fresh
   basil, or 1 teaspoon
   dried, crushed
2 teaspoons sugar
1/2 teaspoon salt
1/4 teaspoon black pepper
Several dashes bottled hot
   pepper sauce, optional

3 tablespoons grated
Parmesan cheese

Combine herb dressing ingredients, stir well and reserve.

Cook pasta twists according to package directions. Drain, rinse with cool water and drain again. Place in a 2-quart bowl.

Cook broccoli, covered, 1 1/2 minutes in microwave oven, or until crispy-tender. Leave the broccoli uncooked, if you prefer.

Add vegetables and chicken to pasta. Stir dressing well and pour over all. Toss. Chill. Toss again and sprinkle Parmesan over top just before serving.

Makes 6 servings, approximately 1-cup each.

Tips...

Serve with fresh fruit and crusty bread or toast.

You may use tuna, turkey or lean ham instead of the chicken.

Recipe contains a large proportion of monunsatured fat due to the olive oil. Olive oil may be helpful in lowering cholesterol.

Analysis: (Each serving)

Calories	261
Total Fat	11.9 grams
Saturated Fat	2.1 grams
Monounsat. Fat	7.4 grams
Polyunsat. Fat	1.3 grams
Cholesterol	22 mgs
Sodium	260 mgs

Ham and Pasta Salad

8 ounces macaroni twists,
(about 3 cups,
uncooked)
1 package (16-ounce)
frozen broccoli,
carrots, water
chestnuts
combination
6 ounces lean cured ham,
diced (about 1 cup)
1 green or red pepper,
diced
1/2 cup chopped fresh
parsley
1 teaspoon dried
basil leaves
1/2 cup part-skim
ricotta cheese
1/2 cup nonfat yogurt
3 tablespoons olive oil
1 1/2 tablespoons wine
vinegar
1 teaspoon salt

1/2 teaspoon black pepper
1/4 cup grated Parmesan
cheese
1 cup sliced red onion

Cook macaroni twists according to package directions. Drain, rinse in cool water and drain again.

Cook frozen vegetables according to package directions. Drain, and cut large pieces to bite size. Add vegetables, ham, green or red pepper, parsley and basil leaves to macaroni.

Combine ricotta cheese, yogurt, oil, vinegar, salt and pepper. Add to macaroni mixture; toss to coat. Chill.

Just before serving sprinkle with Parmesan cheese and garnish with red onion slices.

Makes 10 servings of about 1 cup each.

Tips...

Garnish with tomato wedges instead of the onion, if you prefer.

Serve with fresh fruit and crusty bread.

Analysis: (Each serving)

Calories	206
Total Fat	7.5 grams
Saturated Fat	2.0 grams
Monounsat. Fat	4.0 grams
Polyunsat. Fat	0.6 grams
Cholesterol	15 mgs
Sodium	516 mgs

Tuna Salad

1 can (6 1/2-ounce) water
   packed tuna, drained
1 hard cooked egg,
   chopped
1/2 cup diced apple
10 dill pickle slices,
   chopped
2 tablespoons reduced
   calorie mayonnaise
   or mayonnaise
   type salad dressing
1 teaspoon prepared
   mustard

Combine all ingredients.

Makes 3 servings.

Tips...

*Add chopped celery, onion
or green pepper as desired.*

*Makes enough for 3
generous sandwiches on
whole wheat bread with lettuce or spinach leaves,
sliced tomatoes, and alfalfa
sprouts. Serve with raw carrot sticks.*

Analysis: (Each serving)

Calories	137
Total Fat	5.1 grams
Saturated Fat	1.1 grams
Monounsat. Fat	1.5 grams
Polyunsat. Fat	1.8 grams
Cholesterol	119 mgs
Sodium	547 mgs

Asparagus with Lemon

1 pound fresh asparagus
2 teaspoons olive oil
1 teaspoon lemon juice
1/8 teaspoon salt
1/8 teaspoon
    black pepper

Break off and discard tough bottom end of each asparagus stalk. Place in single or double layer in microwave casserole.

Add 2 tablespoons water and cook, covered, on full power 4 minutes or until tender but crisp to the bite. Rearrange asparagus one time while cooking.

Drain asparagus. Combine olive oil and lemon juice; sprinkle on asparagus. Add salt and pepper, if desired.

May be served warm or at room temperature.

Makes 4 servings.

Tips...

If asparagus are sandy, let them soak a few minutes in cold water before cooking, or scrape stems with a vegetable peeler.

Analysis: (Each serving)

Calories	44
Total Fat	2.8 grams
Saturated Fat	0.4 grams
Monounsat. Fat	1.7 grams
Polyunsat. Fat	0.3 grams
Cholesterol	0.0 mgs
Sodium	70 mgs

Snap Beans With Onion

**1 pound fresh
green beans,
ends and strings
removed
1/2 cup chopped onion
2 tablespoons water
2 teaspoons margarine
1/2 teaspoon salt
1/8 teaspoon black
pepper**

Combine beans with a small amount of boiling salted water. Cook in covered saucepan on range surface unit 15 to 20 minutes until tender.

Meanwhile, combine chopped onion and the two tablespoons water in a 1 1/2 quart microwave casserole. Cook, covered, 3 minutes or until onion is tender.

Add cooked drained beans to onion. Season with margarine, salt, and pepper.

Makes 5 servings.

Tips...

Fresh green beans are better cooked on the surface unit of a conventional range. Microwave-cooked green beans can end up quite crunchy unless the beans are very young and tender.

Frozen green beans cook well in a microwave oven.

Analysis: (Each serving)

Calories	50
Total Fat	1.7 grams
Saturated Fat	0.3 grams
Monounsat. Fat	0.7 grams
Polyunsat. Fat	0.7 grams
Cholesterol	0.0 mgs
Sodium	230 mgs

Pickled Beets with Vinegar

1 (14-ounce) can
  sliced beets
1/4 cup white vinegar

Discard 1/4 cup liquid from the can of beets.

Pour beets and remaining liquid in a bowl and add 1/4 cup vinegar.

Chill several hours before serving. Beets will keep, covered, in refrigerator for one week.

Makes 4 servings.

Tips...

Pickled beets may be diced and added to combination salad.

Analysis: (Each serving)

Calories	18
Total Fat	0.0 gram
Cholesterol	0.0 mgs
Sodium	155 mgs

Fresh Broccoli with Oil and Lemon

❖ MICROWAVE

1 pound broccoli
2 tablespoons water
2 teaspoons olive oil
1 teaspoon
    lemon juice
1/4 teaspoon salt
1/8 teaspoon pepper

Wash broccoli and discard tough portions of stalk.

Split stalks lengthwise to uniform size for more even cooking.

For a more tender broccoli, peel stalks with a paring knife before cooking.

Arrange broccoli spears with stalks to outside of dish and flowerets in center. Add water.

Cover and cook on full power 6 to 7 minutes. Let stand covered three minutes.

Just before serving, sprinkle olive oil, lemon juice and salt and pepper over broccoli.

Makes 4 servings.

Tips...

Broccoli is one of the few vegetables that contain calcium. It also contains fiber, Vitamin A and Vitamin C, all of which help protect against heart disease and cancer.

Analysis: (Each serving)

Calories	51
Total Fat	3.1 grams
Saturated Fat	0.4 grams
Monounsat. Fat	1.7 grams
Polyunsat. Fat	0.4 grams
Cholesterol	0.0 mgs
Sodium	164 mgs

Quick Cooked Cabbage

❖ *MICROWAVE*

**4 cups shredded
  cabbage
2 tablespoons water
2 teaspoons margarine
1/4 teaspoon salt
1/8 teaspoon
  black pepper
Dash red wine vinegar,
  optional**

Place cabbage and water in covered microwave oven casserole.

Cook on full power 5 to 6 minutes, stirring once.

Stir in remaining ingredients.

Makes 4 servings.

Tips...

Cabbage, along with broc-coli, cauliflower, rutabagas and turnips are cruciferous vegetables. They may reduce your risk of cancer. Eat several servings per week.

Analysis: (Each serving)

Calories	32
Total Fat	1.9 grams
Saturated Fat	0.3 grams
Monounsat. Fat	0.8 grams
Polyunsat. Fat	0.8 grams
Cholesterol	0.0 mgs
Sodium	163 mgs

Parsleyed Carrots

5 carrots, peeled and thinly sliced
4 tablespoons water
1/2 teaspoon sugar
1/4 teaspoon salt
2 teaspoons margarine
2 teaspoons chopped fresh parsley

Place carrots, water, sugar, and salt in 1-quart microwave casserole.

Cook, covered, on full power 7 to 9 minutes until carrots are tender. Stir several times while cooking.

Add margarine and parsley.

Makes 5 servings.

Tips...

When cooking in a microwave oven, stir small, loose vegetables from outside to center to distribute heat. Foods around outside edges get more intense cooking.

Analysis: (Each serving)

Calories	47
Total Fat	1.6 grams
Saturated Fat	0.3 grams
Monounsat. Fat	0.7 grams
Polyunsat. Fat	0.6 grams
Cholesterol	0.0 mgs
Sodium	147 mgs

Cauliflower Paprika

1 medium head cauliflower, about 1 1/2 pounds
1/4 cup water
1/2 tablespoon margarine
1/4 teaspoon salt
Dash paprika

Trim leaves and wash cauliflower. Separate into flowers.

Place in microwave-safe casserole with 1/4 cup water.

Cook, covered, on full power about 8 to 10 minutes. Stir one time while cooking.

Season with margarine and salt.

Sprinkle with paprika just before serving.

Makes 6 servings.

Tips...

Sprinkle with chopped parsley or chives before serving, if desired.

Analysis: (Each serving)

Calories	34
Total Fat	1.0 grams
Saturated Fat	0.2 grams
Monounsat. Fat	0.2 grams
Polyunsat. Fat	0.4 grams
Cholesterol	0.0 mgs
Sodium	112 mgs

Corn on the Cob

**Ears of corn ,
still in husk**

Place ears of corn, still in the husk, 1 inch apart in microwave oven.

Cook at full power. Turn corn over one time while cooking.

1 ear	2 to 3 minutes
2 ears	4 to 6 minutes
4 ears	8 to 10 minutes

Let corn stand 5 to 10 minutes before removing husks and silk.

Season each ear of corn with 3/4 teaspoon margarine.

Tips...

To cook fresh corn with husks and silk removed, place corn in microwave-safe dish with 2 to 4 tablespoons water; cover. Time as above.

Analysis: (Each ear, approx
. 5-inches long)

Calories	110
Total Fat	3.8 grams
Saturated Fat	0.7 grams
Monounsat. Fat	1.5 grams
Polyunsat. Fat	1.5 grams
Cholesterol	0.0 mgs
Sodium	88 mgs

Southern Okra

1 1/4 cups, okra cut
in 1/4-inch
slices (about
6-ounces)
1/2 cup chopped
green pepper
1/4 cup finely
chopped onion
2 tablespoons water
1 (15-ounce) can
cut-up tomatoes
3/4 teaspoon sugar
1/4 teaspoon
black pepper

Place okra, green pepper, onion and water in a microwave-safe casserole.

Cook, covered, 5 to 7 minutes until vegetables are done to your taste. Stir one time while cooking.

Add tomatoes, sugar and pepper, stirring gently.

Cook, covered, 2 more minutes, or until heated through.

Makes 6 servings.

Tips...

When a recipe calls for cooking onion in a small amount of fat, cook it in the microwave using several tablespoons of water instead.

Analysis: (Each serving)

Calories	29
Total Fat	0.3 grams
Saturated Fat	0.0 grams
Monounsat. Fat	0.0 grams
Polyunsat. Fat	0.1 grams
Cholesterol	0 mgs
Sodium	124 mgs

Baked Acorn Squash

❖ *MICROWAVE*

**1 whole squash,
about 1 pound
2 teaspoons margarine
2 teaspoons brown sugar
2/3 cup unsweetened
applesauce
1/4 teaspoon cinnamon**

With a fork or small paring knife, pierce squash in several places to its center.

Place squash on paper towel or plate in microwave oven.

Cook on full power 10 minutes or until squash is soft; turn squash over one time while cooking.

Let stand 5 minutes.

Cut squash in half lengthwise, remove seeds.

Place 1 teaspoon margarine and brown sugar in each half, spreading evenly.

Place applesauce in each squash cavity and sprinkle cinnamon over all.

Reheat 1 or 2 minutes, if desired.

Makes 2 servings.

Tips...

Cranberry sauce may be substituted for the applesauce.

Analysis: (Each half)

Calories	126
Total Fat	4.2 grams
Saturated Fat	0.8 grams
Monounsat. Fat	1.7 grams
Polyunsat. Fat	1.6 grams
Cholesterol	0.0 mgs
Sodium	38 mgs

Summer Squash with Herbs

❖ *MICROWAVE*

**1 1/2 pounds zucchini
or yellow squash**
2 tablespoons water
**1 teaspoon instant
chopped onion**
1 teaspoon parsley flakes
1/2 teaspoon basil
1/4 teaspoon oregano
1/4 teaspoon salt

Wash squash well to remove soil, but do not peel. Cut in 1/4-inch slices, and place in a 2-quart microwave-safe casserole. Add remaining ingredients, stirring to coat.

Cook, covered, on full power 8 to 10 minutes until squash is tender, stirring once.

Makes 6 servings.

Tips...

Summer Squash with Cherry Tomatoes:

Prepare as above. When squash is tender, add 1 pint cherry tomatoes. Cook, covered, 3 minutes longer to heat the tomatoes.

Analysis: (Each serving)

Calories	22
Total Fat	0.6 grams
Saturated Fat	0.1 grams
Monounsat. Fat	0.0 grams
Polyunsat. Fat	0.1 grams
Cholesterol	0.0 mgs
Sodium	90 mgs

Spaghetti Squash

**1 spaghetti squash
(about 2 pounds)**

Cut squash in half lengthwise; remove seeds and membrane. Place squash halves side by side, cut side down, in baking dish. Add 1/4 cup water. Cover with plastic wrap.

Cook on full power for 14 to 16 minutes, or until squash is tender. Let stand 10 minutes.

With a fork, remove the spaghetti-like strands from the squash shell.

Makes 4 cups, approximately.

Tips...

Serve squash with spaghetti sauce, or serve plain with margarine, salt and pepper.

Vegetables are usually cooked on full power in the microwave oven. A cover helps speed cooking and keeps them moist.

Analysis: (Each 1/2 cup serving)

Calories	23
Total Fat	0.7 grams
Saturated Fat	0.1 grams
Monounsat. Fat	0.0 grams
Polyunsat. Fat	0.1 grams
Cholesterol	1.0 mgs
Sodium	0 mgs

Baked Tomatoes

6 firm medium-sized
   tomatoes
1/2 teaspoon salt
1/2 teaspoon
   black pepper
2 1/2 tablespoons
   chopped parsley
1 tablespoon chopped
   fresh basil, or
   1 teaspoon dried
1 clove garlic, minced
1 tablespoon olive oil

Oil large shallow baking dish.

Cut tomatoes horizontally and place cut-side up in the dish.

Sprinkle with salt and pepper.

Combine parsley, basil, and garlic and sprinkle over the tomatoes.

Drizzle 1/4 teaspoon of oil on each tomato half.

Bake at 400-degrees 20 to 25 minutes.

Serve warm or room temperature.

Makes 6 servings, 1 tomato each.

Tips...

Do not peel tomatoes or they will fall apart.

Analysis: (Each tomato)

Calories	48
Total Fat	2.4 grams
Saturated Fat	0.3 grams
Monounsat. Fat	1.7 grams
Polyunsat. Fat	0.3 grams
Cholesterol	0.0 mgs
Sodium	189 mgs

Sliced Potatoes with Onion

3 medium potatoes,
about 1 pound
1/4 cup finely
chopped onion
3 tablespoons water
1 tablespoon margarine
1/4 teaspoon salt
1/4 teaspoon
black pepper
1 tablespoon
chopped parsley

Scrub potatoes, but do not peel.

Cut potatoes in rounds approximately 1/4-inch thick.

Place potatoes, onion and water in microwave casserole; stir to combine.

Cook, covered, on full power 10 to 12 minutes, or until potatoes are fork tender. Stir several times while cooking.

Stir in remaining ingredients.

Makes 4 servings.

Tips...

Potato skins turn green if exposed to too much light. Trim any green areas before cooking.

Analysis: (Each serving)

Calories	140
Total Fat	2.9 grams
Saturated Fat	0.6 grams
Monounsat. Fat	1.3 grams
Polyunsat. Fat	1.1 grams
Cholesterol	0.0 mgs
Sodium	168 mgs

Parsley Buttered New Potatoes

❖ *MICROWAVE*

**1 1/2 pound small
new potatoes**
3 tablespoons water
2 tablespoons margarine
**1 tablespoon
chopped parsley**
2 teaspoons lemon juice
1/4 teaspoon salt
1/4 teaspoon pepper

Scrub potatoes and cut a band of skin from middle of each.

Place potatoes and water in a covered microwave-safe dish.

Cook on full power 8 to 10 minutes, or until fork tender, stirring once.

Add remaining ingredients, stirring to combine.

Makes 6 servings.

PARSLEY

Tips...

New Potatoes and Peas:

Place contents of 1 (10-ounce) box frozen peas in a casserole dish with 1/4 cup water. Cook, covered, on full power 6 to 7 minutes stirring once. Add 1/4 teaspoon salt and 2 teaspoons margarine. Combine peas with the parsley buttered new potatoes.

Analysis: (Each serving)

Calories	144
Total Fat	3.8 grams
Saturated Fat	0.7 grams
Monounsat. Fat	1.7 grams
Polyunsat. Fat	1.4 grams
Cholesterol	0.0 mgs
Sodium	130 mgs

Easy Scalloped Potatoes

**3 medium potatoes,
cooked and sliced
(1 pound uncooked)**
1 1/2 tablespoons flour
**1 teaspoon instant
minced onion**
1/2 teaspoon salt
**1/8 teaspoon
black pepper**
1 1/4 cups skim milk
**1 1/2 tablespoons
margarine**
Paprika
Chopped parsley, optional

Place a layer of sliced potatoes in a 2-quart casserole.

Sprinkle a layer of flour, salt and pepper over potatoes. Add onion. Continue layers until all potatoes are used.

Pour milk over all making sure the flour is moistened. Dot with margarine.

Cook, covered, on full power 7 minutes or until sauce thickens, stirring once. Cooking time will depend on the starting temperature of the potatoes.

Sprinkle with paprika, and chopped parsley if desired.

Makes 4 servings.

Tips...

Be sure to use a deep 2-quart casserole. Milk boils vigorously in the microwave oven.

Analysis: (Each serving)

Calories	163
Total Fat	4.4 grams
Saturated Fat	0.9 grams
Monounsat. Fat	1.9 grams
Polyunsat. Fat	1.6 grams
Cholesterol	1.0 mgs
Sodium	349 mgs

Waffle Potatoes

**2 large potatoes,
8-ounces each
1 tablespoon
vegetable oil**

Wash and dry potatoes; cut them in half lengthwise.

Score tops in 1/2-inch squares, making cuts 1/2-inch deep.

Rub skins and tops with oil; sprinkle remaining oil over tops.

Place potatoes in a shallow pan and bake in a hot oven (450-degrees) 40 minutes, or until potatoes are golden brown and tender.

Makes 4 servings of 1/2 potato each.

Tips...

Spinkle tops of potatoes with paprika or chili powder just before serving.

Almost everyone eats skin and all when potatoes are prepared this way.

Analysis: (1/2 potato)

Calories	141
Totat Fat	3.6 grams
Saturated Fat	0.5 grams
Monounsat. Fat	0.9 grams
Polyunsat. Fat	2.1 grams
Cholesterol	0.0 mgs
Sodium	8 mgs

QUICK BREADS

The breads in this section provide a little sweetness along with some essential nutrients. Nuts are added in mimimal amounts; they are high in calories and fat.

When the recipe calls for eggs, you may use the egg substitutes available at the supermarket, if desired. Egg substitutes contain no cholesterol.

Oatmeal-Raisin Muffins

1 1/3 tablespoons vinegar
1 cup (approximately) skim milk
1 cup quick cooking oatmeal
1/3 cup raisins
2 egg whites
1/3 cup brown sugar
1/4 cup vegetable oil
1 cup all-purpose flour
1 teaspoon baking powder
1/2 teaspoon baking soda
1 teaspoon cinnamon
1/4 teaspoon salt

Place vinegar in a 1-cup measure; add milk to make 1 cup. Let sit 1 or 2 minutes to "sour".

In a large bowl, soak oatmeal and raisins in the sour milk about 30 minutes or until part of the milk is absorbed.

Add egg whites and beat well. Mix in the sugar and oil.

Blend flour with remaining dry ingredients. Add flour mixture all at once to oatmeal mixture. Stir only until flour is moistened; batter should appear lumpy.

Spoon batter into greased muffin pans.

Bake in preheated 400-degree oven 14 to 18 minutes until toothpick inserted near center of muffin comes out dry.

Makes 12 muffins.

Tips...

To measure flour, fluff with a fork, spoon flour into measuring cup, and level with a spatula.

Muffins freeze well.

Oatmeal-Blueberry Muffins:

Omit raisins. Gently stir in 3/4 cup fresh or frozen blueberries after adding flour. Bake as above.

Analysis: (Each muffin)

Calories	146
Fat	5.1 grams
Saturated Fat	0.7 gram
Monounsat. Fat	1.3 grams
Polyunsat. Fat	2.9 grams
Cholesterol	0.0 mgs
Sodium	126 mgs

Applesauce Nut Bread

1 cup all-purpose flour
1 cup whole wheat flour
3/4 cup sugar
1/3 cup chopped walnuts
1 tablespoon baking
　powder
1 1/2 teaspoons cinnamon
1/2 teaspoon baking soda
1/2 teaspoon salt
1 egg, beaten
1 1/4 cups unsweetened
　applesauce
1/4 cup vegetable oil

Combine all dry ingredients, including nuts, in a large bowl; stir well to blend.

In a small bowl, combine egg, applesauce and oil.

Add egg mixture to dry ingredients; stir until blended.

Bake in a greased 9 x 5-inch loaf pan at 350-degrees for approximately 50 minutes, or until a toothpick inserted near center of loaf comes out dry.

Cool 10 minutes before removing from pan.

Makes 1 loaf, 18 slices.

Tips...

Smaller slices may be desirable; two small slices can appear to be more than one large slice. For two smaller loaves, bake half the batter in each of two 8 1/2 x 3 1/2-inch loaf pans for 25 to 30 minutes.

If glass pan is used for baking bread, reduce oven temperature by 25-degrees.

You may use 2 cups of all-purpose flour instead of 1 cup all-purpose and 1 cup whole wheat. You get a little extra fiber and several extra nutrients with the whole wheat flour.

Bread freezes well.

Analysis: (Each slice)

Calories	132
Total Fat	4.9 grams
Saturated Fat	0.6 grams
Monounsat. Fat	1.2 grams
Polyunsat. Fat	2.8 grams
Cholesterol	15 mgms
Sodium	136 mgs

Banana-Nut Bread

1 1/2 cups all-purpose
  flour
1 1/2 cups whole wheat
  flour
1 1/2 cups sugar
1/3 cup coarsely chopped
  walnuts
2 cups mashed bananas,
  about 5 medium
2/3 cup vegetable oil
2 teaspoons baking soda
1/2 teaspoon salt
1/2 teaspoon baking
  powder
4 eggs
2 teaspoons vanilla
  extract

Heat oven to 350-degrees. Grease bottoms only of 2 loaf pans, 9x5x3 or 8 1/2x4 1/2x2 1/2-inches.

Beat all ingredients on low speed, scraping bowl constantly, 30 seconds. Beat on medium speed, scraping bowl frequently, 45 seconds. Pour into pans.

Bake until wooden pick inserted near center comes out clean, 50 to 60 minutes.

Cool 10 minutes; loosen sides of loaves and remove from pans.

Cool completely before slicing. Wrap tightly and store at room temperature up to 4 days, or refrigerate up to 10 days. Freeze for longer storage.

Makes two loaves, 18 slices per loaf.

Tips...

Bread freezes well.

Slice bread before freezing; remove only amount needed at one time.

Recipe may be halved.

Extra bananas on hand? Mash and freeze in one-cup portions. To use, thaw gently in microwave oven and use immediately after thawing.

Analysis: (Each slice)

Calories	136
Total fat	5.6 grams
Saturated Fat	0.8 grams
Monounsat. Fat	1.4 grams
Polyunsat. Fat	3.0 grams
Cholesterol	30 mgs
Sodium	89 mgs

Cranberry Nut Bread

1 cup all-purpose flour
1 cup whole wheat flour
3/4 cup sugar
1 1/2 teaspoons baking
    powder
1/2 teaspoon baking soda
1/2 teaspoon salt
3 tablespoons margarine
3/4 cup orange juice
1 egg, well beaten
1 tablespoon grated
    orange peel
1 cup cranberries, fresh
    or frozen,
    coarsely chopped
1/3 cup chopped pecans

Preheat oven to 350-degrees.

In a large bowl mix together flour, sugar, baking powder, soda and salt. Cut in margarine.

Stir in orange juice, egg, and orange peel mixing just to moisten. Fold in cranberries and nuts.

Spoon into well greased and lightly floured 9x5x3 inch loaf pan. Bake 50 to 60 minutes or until toothpick inserted in center comes out clean.

Cool on a rack 15 minutes. Remove from pan, cool completely. Wrap and store overnight before slicing.

Makes 1 loaf, 18 slices.

Tips...

Purchase extra cranberries in season. Freeze in original wrapper in another plastic bag. Use as needed.

Bread freezes well.

To measure all-purpose flour fluff with a fork, spoon into measuring cup and level with spatula. To measure whole wheat flour, spoon into measuring cup and level with spatula.

Analysis: (Each slice)

Calories	120
Total Fat	3.8 grams
Saturated Fat	0.6 grams
Monounsat. Fat	1.8 grams
Polyunsat. Fat	1.2 grams
Cholesterol	15 mgs
Sodium	130 mgs

Pumpkin Nut Bread

3 cups whole wheat flour
1 3/4 cups sugar
1/2 cup raisins
1/3 cup coarsely chopped
  pecans
1/2 cup vegetable oil
2 teaspoons cinnamon
2 teaspoons baking soda
1/2 teaspoon salt
1/2 teaspoon baking
  powder
4 eggs
1 (16-ounce) can pumpkin
2 teaspoons vanilla

Heat oven to 350-degrees. Grease bottoms only of 2 loaf pans, 9x5x3 or 8 1/2x4 1/2x2 1/2.

Beat all ingredients in large bowl on low speed, scraping bowl constantly, 30 seconds.

Beat on medium speed, scraping bowl frequently, 45 seconds. Pour into pans.

Bake 50 to 60 minutes or until toothpick inserted in center of bread comes out clean. Cool 10 minutes before removing from pan.

Cool completely before slicing. Wrap tightly and store at room temperature up to 4 days, or refrigerate up to 10 days.

Makes 2 loaves, 18 slices per loaf.

Tips...

Recipe may be halved. Bread and muffins freeze well.

Pumpkin Nut Muffins:

Prepare batter as above. Grease bottoms only of medium muffin cups. Fill cups about 3/4 full. Bake until tops spring back when touched lightly, 20 to 25 minutes. Makes 2 1/2 dozen muffins.

Analysis: (Each slice)

Calories	130
Total Fat	4.7 grams
Saturated Fat	0.7 grams
Monounsat. Fat	1.5 grams
Polyunsat. Fat	2.1 grams
Cholesterol	30 mgs
Sodium	90 mgs

130

DESSERTS

Dessert recipes in this section will satisfy the taste for sweets and will also provide some nutrients. Most are low calorie versions of the original recipes. Where the amount of sugar is decreased, cinnamon or vanilla is added to enhance flavor.

Other low-fat choices are angel food cake with fresh strawberries, nonfat frozen yogurt, ice milk or sherbet.

Baked Apple Slices

1 large apple
1 1/2 teaspoons
    margarine
1 1/2 teaspoons sugar
1/8 teaspoon cinnamon

Remove core from apple; peel if desired.

Cut apple in horizontal slices about 1/2 inch thick. Place slices in baking dish.

Dot with margarine, sprinkle with sugar and cinnamon, and cover with wax paper.

Cook at full power 3 minutes, or until apple is tender.

Makes 2 servings.

Tips...

May be served as a side dish or dessert.

Baked Apple:

Core apple to within 1/2-inch of end. Remove about 1/2-inch of peel from top. Place apple in small bowl; place seasonings in core, cover with waxed paper and cook 3-4 minutes until tender.

Analysis: (Each serving)	
Calories	99
Total Fat	3.3 grams
Saturated Fat	0.6 grams
Monounsat. Fat	1.3 grams
Polyunsat. Fat	1.1 grams
Cholesterol	0.0 mgs
Sodium	25 mgs

Curried Fruit

1 (20-ounce) can
pineapple chunks
in juice, drained
1 (16-ounce) can apricot
halves in light sirup,
drained
2 tablespoons raisins
1 tablespoon margarine
2 tablespoons
brown sugar
1/4 teaspoon cinnamon
1/4 teaspoon curry
powder, or to taste

Place fruits in baking dish.

Melt margarine on full power (about 20 seconds) in a 1-cup measure.

Add sugar and spices, cook 20 seconds longer. Pour over fruit; stir gently to combine.

Cook on full power 4 minutes, or until heated through, stirring once.

Makes 8 servings.

Tips...

Serve as a side dish with chicken or ham, or serve as a dessert.

Analysis: (Each serving)

Calories	79
Total Fat	1.4 grams
Saturated Fat	0.3 grams
Monounsat. Fat	0.6 grams
Polyunsat. Fat	0.5 grams
Cholesterol	0.0 mgs
Sodium	16 mgs

Oranges in Liqueur

6 navel oranges
4 tablespoons sugar
3 tablespoons
Maraschino
or orange liqueur
Grated peel of 1 orange

Peel four of the oranges being careful to remove all the white membrane; slice oranges horizontally in 1/4-inch slices. Place slices in bowl.

Grate peel of one orange; combine peel with the juice of the other 2 oranges, sugar, and liqueur. Pour over orange slices.

Refrigerate 4 hours or overnight.

Makes 6 servings.

Tips...

A refreshing dessert after a generous meal.

To get more juice from oranges or lemons, microwave whole fruits on full power 30 seconds each. Let stand 2 or 3 minutes before cutting.

Analysis: (Each serving)

Calories	100
Total Fat	0.0 mgs
Cholesterol	0.0 mgs
Sodium	1 mgs

Fresh Apple Crisp

6 cups peeled,
   sliced apples
1/4 cup plus
   2 tablespoons
   brown sugar,
   packed
2 tablespoons flour
3 tablespoons water
1 teaspoon vanilla
2 tablespoons melted
   margarine
3/4 cup oatmeal, regular
   or quick-cooking
1 teaspoon cinnamon

Preheat oven to 350-degrees.

Place fruit in 8-inch square baking dish. Combine 2 tablespoons brown sugar with the flour, water and vanilla. Add to fruit, stirring to coat.

Add melted margarine to oatmeal; stir to moisten. Add remaining brown sugar and cinnamon to oatmeal, stir to combine.

Top fruit with oatmeal mixture. Bake 40 to 50 minutes or until fruit is tender.

Makes 9 servings.

Tips...

To melt margarine, place in a 1-cup glass measure and heat in microwave oven for about 25 seconds.

Fresh Peach or Fresh Pear Crisp:

Substitute fresh peaches or pears for the apples.
Prepare and cook as above.

Analysis: (Each serving)

Calories	130
Total Fat	2.9 grams
Saturated Fat	0.6 grams
Monounsat. Fat	1.2 grams
Polyunsat. Fat	1.1 grams
Cholesterol	0.0 mgs
Sodium	27 mgs

Peach Crisp

5 cups sliced fresh
   peaches
1 teaspoon vanilla
1/3 cup brown sugar,
   packed, divided
1/4 cup flour, divided
1/4 cup quick cooking
   oatmeal
1 teaspoon cinnamon,
2 tablespoons margarine,
   melted

Place fruit in a 9-inch round baking dish. Sprinkle with vanilla, 2 tablespoons of brown sugar and 1 tablespoon of flour; toss to coat.

In a small bowl, combine remaining sugar, flour, oatmeal and cinnamon. Add melted margarine; stir until mixture is moistened. Sprinkle evenly over fruit.

Cook at full power 12 to 15 minutes, or until fruit is tender and mixture is bubbly throughout. Rotate dish 1/2 turn halfway through cooking time.

Makes 8 servings.

Tips...

For even cooking, raise the fruit crisp off the oven floor, by placing the pan with fruit crisp on an over-turned saucer or glass pie plate.

Analysis: (Each serving)

Calories	130
Total Fat	3.1 grams
Saturated Fat	0.5 grams
Monounsat. Fat	1.4 grams
Polyunsat. Fat	1.1 grams
Cholesterol	0 mgs
Sodium	29 mgs

Vanilla Pudding

1 (12-ounce) can evaporated skimmed milk 1/2 cup water 1/3 cup sugar 3 tablespoons cornstarch 1 egg, beaten 1 teaspoon vanilla extract	Pour milk and water into saucepan. Blend sugar and cornstarch together and add to milk mixture, stirring until dry ingredients are dissolved. Cook over medium-low heat, stirring often, until mixture comes to a full boil; boil 1 minute. Mixture should begin to thicken. Remove from heat.

Stir 1/2 cup of the hot mixure into the beaten egg; then add egg mixture to saucepan. Heat over low heat, stirring constantly, until thick.

Remove from heat and stir in vanilla. Pour into bowl and chill.

Makes 5 servings, 1/2 cup each.

❖ *Alternate MICROWAVE cooking instructions:*

Place milk, sugar and cornstarch in a 1-quart measure. Cook on full power, about 5 minutes until mixture boils 1 minute and begins to thicken, stirring 3 or 4 times. Blend in egg as above, and cook on 1/2 power 1 to 1 1/2 minutes until thick, stirring every 30 seconds. Continue as above.

Tips...

Canned evaporated skimmed milk is available at the supermarket adjacent to the regular canned evaporated milk.

Stirring with a wire whisk helps prevent lumps.

Banana Pudding:

Follow above recipe except add 2/3 cup water instead of 1/2 cup. When pudding is cooked, layer in serving bowl with 1 sliced banana and 10 vanilla wafers. Crumble 2 additional vanilla wafers and sprinkle over the top layer of pudding.

Analysis: (Each 1/2 cup serving)

Calories	145
Total Fat	1.5 grams
Saturated Fat	0.4 grams
Monounsat. Fat	0.5 grams
Polyunsat. Fat	0.1 grams
Cholesterol	58 mgs
Sodium	102 mgs

Almond Cream

3/4 cup cold water
1 enveloped unflavored
  gelatin
1/3 cup sugar
3/4 cup boiling water
1 1/4 cups evaporated
  skim milk
1/2 teaspoon
  vanilla extract
1/2 teaspoon
  almond extract
Fresh fruit slices,
  optional
	Sprinkle gelatin over cold water in medium bowl. Let stand 1 minute.
	
	Add sugar and stir until gelatin starts to dissolve. Pour boiling water over gelatin mixture and stir until gelatin dissolves.
	
	Add milk, vanilla, and almond extract.
	
	Pour mixture into 5 serving bowls.
	
	Chill until set, about 3 hours.
	
	Makes 5 servings, about 1/2 cup each.

Tips...

To serve, arrange several slices of fresh fruit on each dessert; choose from peaches, bananas, kiwi, strawberries.

Or, sprinkle toasted slivered almonds over top.

Analysis: (Each serving)

Calories	106
Total Fat	0.3 grams
Saturated Fat	0.1 grams
Monounsat. Fat	0.1 grams
Polyunsat. Fat	0.0 grams
Cholesterol	2 mgs
Sodium	75 mgs

Date Nut Cupcakes

4 ounces chopped dates
(2/3 cup)
1/2 cup boiling water
1/2 cup sugar
1/4 cup (1/2 stick)
margarine, room
temperature
1 egg, room temperature
1 cup flour
1/2 teaspoon baking soda
1/4 teaspoon salt
3 tablespoons
chopped pecans

Combine dates with water; stir well. Let cool to room temperature, stirring occasionally.

Cream margarine with sugar and egg until light.

Combine flour, baking soda, and salt; add to creamed mixture alternately with date mixture mixing just to combine.

Stir in chopped nuts.

Spoon mixture into greased muffin pans.

Bake in preheated 350-degree oven 14 to 18 minutes or until toothpick inserted near center of cupcake comes out dry. Turn out on wire rack to cool.

Makes 12 cupcakes.

Tips...

To measure flour, fluff with a fork, spoon into measuring cup and level off with a spatula.

Sprinkle cooled cupcakes with powdered sugar, if desired.

Cupcakes freeze well.

Analysis: (Each cupcake)

Calories	146
Total Fat	5.4 grams
Saturated Fat	0.9 grams
Monounsat. Fat	2.6 grams
Polyunsat. Fat	1.7 grams
Cholesterol	23 mgs
Sodium	119 mgs

Meringue Cookies

2 large egg whites
3/4 cup sugar
1 teaspoon vanilla

Beat egg whites until foamy.

Gradually add sugar and continue to beat until meringue stands in stiff peaks.

Fold in vanilla.

Drop by teaspoonful about 1-inch apart on well-greased cookie sheet.

Bake in slow oven (250-degrees) 40 to 50 minutes until cookies are firm but not brown.

Remove at once from cookie sheet to wire racks.

When cookies have cooled completely, store in a tightly covered container.

Makes 30 cookies.

Tips...

Eggs are easier to separate when cold but egg whites give greater volume if beaten at room temperature.

Analysis: (Each cookie)

Calories	20
Total Fat	0.0 mgs
Cholesterol	0.0 mgs
Sodium	3 mgs

Oatmeal Fruit Cookies

3/4 cup margarine,
    room temperature
1 cup brown sugar,
    packed
1/2 cup granulated sugar
2 egg whites,
    room temperature
1/4 cup skim milk
1 teaspoon vanilla
1 cup whole wheat flour
1/2 teaspoon baking soda
1 teaspoon cinnamon
1/4 teaspoon nutmeg,
    optional
3 cups quick cooking
    oatmeal
3/4 cup raisins
1/2 cup chopped almonds

Place margarine, sugars, eggwhites, milk, and vanilla in mixing bowl; beat thoroughly.

Blend together flour, baking soda, cinnamon and nutmeg; add to margarine mixture, mixing well.

Stir in oatmeal, raisins, and nuts.

Drop batter a teaspoon at a time onto oiled cookie sheet.

Bake in a preheated 350-degree oven 10 to 12 minutes.

Carefully remove from cookie sheet. Cool on wire rack. Cookies crisp as they cool. Store cooled cookies in tightly covered container.

Makes 6 dozen cookies.

Tips...

Instead of raisins, you may substitute 3/4 cup of diced mixed dried fruit, or 3/4 cup chopped dates.

Cookies freeze well.

Analysis: (Each cookie)

Calories	62
Total Fat	2.5 grams
Saturated Fat	0.4 gram
Monounsat. Fat	1.2 grams
Polyunsat. Fat	0.9 gram
Cholesterol	0.0 mgs
Sodium	26 mgs

Brownie Pudding

1 cup all-purpose flour
2 teaspoons baking
   powder
1/2 teaspoon salt
1/2 cup granulated sugar
2 tablespoons cocoa
1/2 cup skim milk
1 teaspoon vanilla
2 tablespoons
   vegetable oil
3 tablespoons chopped
   almonds
3/4 cup brown sugar
3 tablespoons cocoa
1 3/4 cups hot water

Preheat oven to 350-degrees.

Blend well the flour, baking powder, salt, granulated sugar, and cocoa. Add milk, vanilla and oil; mix until smooth. Add nuts. Spread evenly in a greased 8-inch square cake pan.

Mix brown sugar and cocoa; sprinkle over batter. Pour hot water over entire batter.

Bake 40 to 45 minutes.

Makes 12 servings.

Tips...

Unsweetened cocoa powder contains very little fat as opposed to most chocolate which contains cocoa butter high in saturated fat.

Analysis: (Each serving)

Calories	168
Total Fat	3.7 grams
Saturated Fat	0.5 grams
Monounsat. Fat	1.3 grams
Polyunsat. Fat	1.6 grams
Cholesterol	0.0 mgs
Sodium	158 mgs

et cetera

In this section are a few additional recipes for your enjoyment.

The pizza recipe is one children like to help make. And, fewer than 30 percent of the calories come from fat.

The party mix is a standard recipe but with a method of preparation that allows you to use less margarine.

The cranberry sauce is easy to prepare and tastes delicious.

Twenty Minute Minestrone

1 carrot, diced
1 small onion, chopped
1 rib celery, chopped
3 tablespoons water
4 cups low sodium
chicken broth
1 medium potato, diced
1/2 cup elbow macaroni,
uncooked
1 tomato, diced
1/2 cup shredded
cabbage
1 tablespoon chopped
parsley
1/2 teaspoon basil
leaves
1/2 teaspoon salt
1/4 teaspoon
black pepper

6 tablespoons grated
Parmesan cheese

Combine carrot, onion and celery with the water in a microwave oven safe casserole. Cook, covered, 6 minutes, stirrring once.

Meanwhile, in a large saucepan on range surface unit, bring chicken broth to a boil.

Add carrot mixture and all remaining ingredients. Simmer, uncovered, 20 minutes or until potato is tender.

Serve in bowls with Parmesan cheese sprinkled over top.

Makes 6 cups or 3 main dish servings.

Tips...

To release aromatic oils, crush dry herb leaves such as basil between fingers before adding.

Vary the vegetables as desired. Zucchini, peas, green beans, or cooked dry beans may be used.

Serve with fresh fruit and whole wheat toast.

Analysis: (Each serving
with cheese)

Calories	239
Total Fat	6.8 grams
Saturated Fat	2.6 grams
Monounsat. Fat	1.7 grams
Polyunsat. Fat	0.9 grams
Cholesterol	8.0 mgs
Sodium	648 mgs

Potato Soup

❖ *MICROWAVE*

3 medium potatoes,
(1 pound) peeled
and diced
1/2 cup finely chopped
onion
1/2 cup water
2 tablespoons flour
2 cups skim milk
1/2 teaspoon salt
1/4 teaspoon
black pepper
1 tablespoon
margarine
1 teaspoon parsley
leaves

Combine potatoes, onions and water in a 2-quart microwave safe dish.

Cook, covered, on full power, 10 minutes or until potatoes are tender. Stir one time.

Lightly mash potatoes.

Stir in flour. Add milk, salt and pepper.

Cover, and cook on full power 5 minutes longer, stirring every minute, or until soup boils and is thickened.

Just before serving add the tablespoon of margarine and the parsley.

Makes 5 servings.

Tips...

Serve with 1/2 tuna salad sandwich on whole wheat toast with lettuce and tomatoes.

Analysis: (Each serving)

Calories	143
Total Fat	2.5 grams
Saturated Fat	0.5 grams
Monounsat. Fat	1.1 grams
Polyunsat. Fat	0.9 grams
Cholesterol	2 mgs
Sodium	287 mgs

Fresh Cranberry Sauce

1 1/2 cups sugar
3/4 cup water
1 (12-ounce) package
    fresh cranberries

Place sugar and water in 3-quart casserole, stirring to dissolve sugar.

Wash cranberries, remove soft berries and stems; combine with sugar mixture.

Cover and cook on full power 12 minutes, or until mixture has come to a hard boil and berries have popped open. Stir once or twice while cooking.

Serve warm or cold.

Makes 3 cups, or 12 servings, 1/4 cup each.

Tips...

Serve with baked turkey or chicken.

Be sure to use a 3-quart microwave container or cranberries will boil over.

Extra cranberry sauce keeps several weeks in the refrigerator; freeze for longer storage.

Buy cranberries in season and freeze. Make the sauce at your convenience.

Analysis: (Each 1/4 cup)

Calories	111
Total Fat	0.2 grams
Saturated Fat	0.0 grams
Monounsat. Fat	0.0 grams
Polyunsat. Fat	0.0 grams
Cholesterol	0.0 mgs
Sodium	1 mg

Party Mix

3 tablespoons margarine
2 tablespoons Worcestershire sauce
1/4 teaspoon garlic powder
3 cups toasted oat circles
2 cups wheat chex
2 cups corn chex
1 cup thin pretzel sticks
1/4 cup dry roasted peanuts

Place margarine in 1-cup measure and heat on full power 30 seconds, or until margarine melts.

Stir in Worcestershire sauce and garlic powder.

Place remaining ingredients in a 3-quart microwave baking dish.

Drizzle margarine mixture over cereal; stir until coated.

Heat uncovered, on full power, 4 to 6 minutes, stirring every 2 minutes.

Turn mixture out onto paper towels to cool.

Makes 8 cups, or 16 servings.

Tips...

Recipe may be halved.

Store cooled mix in tightly covered container.

Analysis: (Each half-cup)

Calories	90
Total Fat	3.5 grams
Saturated Fat	0.6 grams
Monounsat. Fat	1.6 grams
Polyunsat. Fat	1.2 grams
Cholesterol	0.0 mgs
Sodium	214 mgs

Whole Wheat Pizza

Crusts:
- 2 to 2 1/2 cups all-purpose flour
- 1 cup whole wheat flour
- 1 teaspoon salt
- 1 package quick-rising yeast
- 1 cup hot water (125 to 130-degrees)
- 2 tablespoons vegetable oil
- Cornmeal

Pizza Sauce:
- 1 (8-ounce) can no-salt-added tomato sauce
- 3 ounces tomato paste (1/2 of a 6-ounce can)
- 1 teaspoon sugar
- 1 teaspoon oregano leaves
- 1 clove garlic, minced

Pizza Topping:
- 8 ounces part-skim mozarella cheese, shredded (2 cups)
- 4 tablespoons grated Parmesan cheese

Chopped green pepper, mushrooms, onions, optional

Set aside 1 cup all-purpose flour. In large bowl, combine remaining all-purpose and whole wheat flour, salt and yeast. Stir hot water and oil into dry ingredients. Mix in only enough of reserved flour to make a soft, but not sticky, dough. Turn out onto lightly floured board; knead until smooth and elastic; about 5 minutes. Cover; let rest 10 minutes.

Punch dough down; divide in half. Using a rolling pin, roll and stretch each half to a 13-inch circle. Place on two 12-inch round pizza pans or 2 baking sheets that have been oiled and sprinkled with cornmeal. Shape edges into a standing rim of dough.

Bake crusts in preheated 450-degree oven for 8 minutes. While dough is cooking, combine pizza sauce ingredients.

Spread each crust with half the pizza sauce and half the mozzarella cheese. Sprinkle each pizza with 2 tablespoons Parmesan cheese.

Bake 10 to 12 minutes more, or until cheese melts and is lightly browned. Cut into wedges to serve. Makes 6 servings at 1/3 pizza each.

Tips...

Water at 125-degrees is very hot to the touch. A quick registering thermometer is a nice kitchen tool to have to check the temperature.

Baked slices of pizza freeze well.

Serve with fresh fruit salad.

Each serving provides over thirty-five percent of an adult's daily calcium requirement.

Analysis: (1/3 pizza)

Calories	437
Total Fat	13.5 grams
Saturated Fat	5.7 grams
Monounsat. Fat	3.6
Polyunsat. Fat	3.4
Cholesterol	23 mgs
Sodium	771 mgs

APPENDIX

Ingredients

Certain ingredients called for in the recipes have equivalents that may be substituted if necessary; other ingredients generally should be used as specified.

Where there is uncertainty about interpretation of ingredients called for in the recipes, recommended choices are given in the paragraph titled "Recommended Ingredients."

Assumptions made in the nutritional content of foods in the recipes are detailed in the "Analysis" paragraph.

General Table of Substitutions

Permissible substitutions for *Recipes For Living* are as follows:

Cornstarch, 1 tablespoon	2 tablespoons flour
Garlic, 1 clove fresh	3/4 teaspoon minced 1/2 teaspoon instant minced garlic or 1/8 teaspoon garlic powder
Herbs, 1 tablespoon fresh	1 teaspoon dried herbs
Lemon juice, fresh	Nothing else provides the same flavor.
Macaroni, uncooked, 1 cup	2 cups cooked
Milk, skim, 1 cup	1/3 cup nonfat dry milk plus water to make 1 cup, or evaporated skimmed milk diluted as directed on the can
Milk, sour milk, 1 cup or buttermilk, 1 cup	1 1/3 tablespoons vinegar or 1 1/2 tablespoons lemon juice plus milk to equal 1 cup, or 1 cup yogurt

Mushrooms, 1 pound raw	6 to 7 ounces canned
Mushrooms, 1 1/3 cups, raw	1/2 cup cooked
Mushrooms, 3 ounces raw	1 cup sliced 1/4-inch thick
Mustard, 1 teaspoon dry	1 tablespoon prepared mustard
Onion, medium (3 per pound)	1 cup chopped
Onion, large (2 per pound)	1 1/2 cups chopped
Onion, fresh chopped, 1 cup	1/4 cup instant chopped onion
Onion, fresh minced, 2 teaspoons	1 teaspoon onion powder
Pepper, sweet green	1 cup diced
Rice, 1 cup long-grain	3 to 4 cups cooked rice
Spaghetti, 8 ounces uncooked	4 to 5 cups cooked

Recommended Ingredients for *Recipes For Living*

Broth, beef or chicken	Canned, prepared with water, or use low-sodium
Cheese, Parmesan	Preferably imported from Italy. Or, use the shredded Parmesan available in sealed packages at the supermarket. Parmesan cheese in the cardboard container does not provide the same flavor.
Eggs	Large size eggs.
Margarine	Oil listed as first ingredient, with a ratio of saturated fat to polyunsaturated fat a minimum of 2 to 4, 4 sticks to the pound.
Meats: Ground round, or extra lean ground beef	15 percent fat or less.
Ground turkey	Should not include turkey skin.
Lean cured ham	Roasted, 5 percent fat or less.

Milk, evaporated skimmed	Canned evaporated milk with fat removed. Dilute only as specified in the recipe.
Oil	Safflower, sunflower, corn, soybean, cottonseed, or canola (rapeseed) oil
Olive oil	Extra-virgin for flavor in salads and vegetables. Any other pure olive oil for cooking.
Pepper, black	Always freshly ground black pepper.
Soy sauce, regular or reduced sodium	Naturally brewed soy sauce.
Wine	Good for drinking, does not have to be expensive.

Nutritional Analyses

Ingredients listed as optional were not included in the nutritional analysis. All pasta and rice products were assumed to be cooked without added salt. Corn oil was used except where the recipe calls for olive oil. Margarine used was 100% corn oil stick margarine. While the nutrition analysis is not exact, where there was a question, more rather than less of an ingredient was accounted for in the analysis so as to err on the conservative side. The primary source of information was U. S. Department of Agriculture, Nutritive Value of Foods, Home and Garden Bulletin Number 72. A computer program utilizing this data was used to analyse the ingredients in each recipe to provide the results given at the bottom of each recipe page. Home and Garden Bulletin No. 72 may be obtained from Superintendent of Documents, U.S. Government Printing Office, Washington, D.C. 20401 $2.75.

For Further Reading:

Coronary Risk Factor Statement for the American Public, American Heart Association, National Center, 7320 Greenville, Dallas 75231. Free.

Dietary Guidelines and Your Diet, seven information bulletins on the recommended Dietary Guidelines for Americans. Order No. 114R. Consumer Information Center-C, P.O. Box 100, Pueblo, Colorado, 81002 $4.50.

Diet, Nutrition and Cancer Prevention: A Guide to Food Choices, National Institutes of Health Publication No. 85-2711. Order by calling toll-free 1-800-4-CANCER. Free.

Eating on the Run, Evelyn Tribole, MS,RD, Life Enhancement Publications, $8.95.

Jane Brody's Good Food Book, Jane E. Brody, W. W. Norton Company, $19.95.

The Fast-Food Guide, Michael Jacobson, Ph.D., Executive Director, Center for Science in the Public Interest, and Sarah Fritschner, Workman Publishing, $4.95.

Tufts University Diet and Nutrition Letter, 53 Park Place, New York, NY 10007, $18 per year.

Cooking Light Magazine, P.O. Box 830549, Birmingham, AL 35282-9810, $12 per year (6 issues).

Index

A

Alcohol, 15, 21, 30 - 32, 46
American Heart Association, 7
Apple Slices, Baked, 132
Apple, Baked, 132
Asparagus with Lemon, 108

B

Baked Apple Slices, 132
Beans, dry
    Creole Beans, 98
    Lentils, 99
    Ranch Style Beans, 97
Beans, Snap, with Onions, 109
Beef
    Beef and Bean Stew, 58
    Beef Strips in Tomato Sauce, 54
    Beef Strogonoff, 55
    Beef with Broccoli, 56
    Beef with Peppers and Tomatoes, 56
    Easy Meat Loaf, 53
    Mexican One-Dish Meal, 52
    Rump Roast Italian Style, 60
    Sloppy Joes, 50
    Spaghetti Squash with Meat Sauce, 51
    Stir-Fry Pepper Steak, 56
    Swiss Steak, 59
    Texas Beef Stew, 57
Beets, Pickled with Vinegar, 110
Bread-Cereal or Grain Group
    daily servings, 18
Breads
    Applesauce Nut Bread, 127
    Banana-Nut Bread, 128
    Cranberry Nut Bread, 129
    Pumpkin Nut Bread, 130
    Whole Wheat Pizza, 148

Breakfast, 25, 26
Broccoli with Oil and Lemon, 111

C

Cabbage, Quick Cooked, 112
Caffeine, 46
Calcium, 18, 23, 40, 46
Calories
    calculating from fats, 39
    in weight gain, 13, 48
    in weight reduction, 13, 47
Cancer, 7
Carbohydrates
    complex, 11, 12, 17, 18
    simple, 12
Carrots, Parsleyed, 113
Cauliflower Paprika, 114
Cheese, 36
Cholesterol, 7
    labeling, 37, 38
    sources, 10, 37
Coconut oil, 11, 37
Cooking tips, 40, 41
Corn on the Cob, 115
Cranberry Sauce, 146

D

Desserts
    Almond Cream, 138
    Apple Crisp, 135
    Apple Slices, Baked, 132
    Apple, Baked, 132
    Banana Pudding, 137
    Brownie Pudding, 142
    Date Nut Cupcakes, 139
    Fruit, Curried, 133
    Meringue Cookies, 140

N

O

P

R

S

T

U

V

W

VMP Services
P.O. Box 713
Arlington, TX 76004

Please send me _____ copies of *Recipes for Living*   @ $9.95 ea. $ _____
Texas residents add sales tax $0.70 ea. $ _____
Postage and handling $1.50 $ _____
TOTAL ENCLOSED $ _____

Name _____

Address_____

City _____ State _____ Zip _____

Make checks payable to VMP Services.

VMP Services
P.O. Box 713
Arlington, TX 76004

Please send me _____ copies of *Recipes for Living*   @ $9.95 ea. $ _____
Texas residents add sales tax $0.70 ea. $ _____
Postage and handling $1.50 $ _____
TOTAL ENCLOSED $ _____

Name _____

Address_____

City _____ State _____ Zip _____

Make checks payable to VMP Services.

VMP Services
P.O. Box 713
Arlington, TX 76004

Please send me _____ copies of *Recipes for Living*   @ $9.95 ea. $ _____
Texas residents add sales tax $0.70 ea. $ _____
Postage and handling $1.50 $ _____
TOTAL ENCLOSED $ _____

Name _____

Address_____

City _____ State _____ Zip _____

Make checks payable to VMP Services.

Reorder Page